Standard Work is a Verb: A Playbook for LEAN Manufacturing

John Allwood

With Bob Pentland

ISBN: 978-0-9975603-0-5

Published By: Lean Leadership Institute Publications
V.P. of Publications: Daniel J. Stanley AAP
Published in the United States of America
First Edition – English

Table of Contents

PREFACE

The book shown below is the second in a series of books under the Lean Leadership Development Model format. Many Lean practitioners are familiar with the world acclaimed, *The Toyota Way*, by Jeffrey K. Liker. This book, released in 2004, established the foundation for Lean implementation. This has been the gold standard by which organizations have implemented the Lean methodology.

In 2014, Dr. Liker and George Trachilis published, *Developing Lean Leaders at All Levels* (http://leanleadership.guru/books/) to give Lean enthusiasts a better chance at finding the right path towards the Toyota Way to Lean Leadership http://toyotawaytoleanleadership.com).

In 2016, Jeff Liker and George Trachilis received the **Shingo Research Award** for *Developing Lean Leaders at All Levels: A Practical Guide*, ranking amongst the best publications in the world of Lean. This book, as an accompaniment to the online course, was developed by Jeff Liker and published by George Trachilis. It represents a complete training system for developing Lean enthusiasts globally. This book, translated into nine languages, is sold to global Universities, spreading the secret to sustaining Lean gains via a coach/learner relationship.

The first book in this series, *OEM Principles of Lean Thinking*, gives an overview of Lean Thinking and the power of seeing all forms of waste. George Trachilis uses critical references from Jim Womack and Dan Jones as he developed his world-renowned online course on the Principles of Lean Thinking, http://lean101.ca.

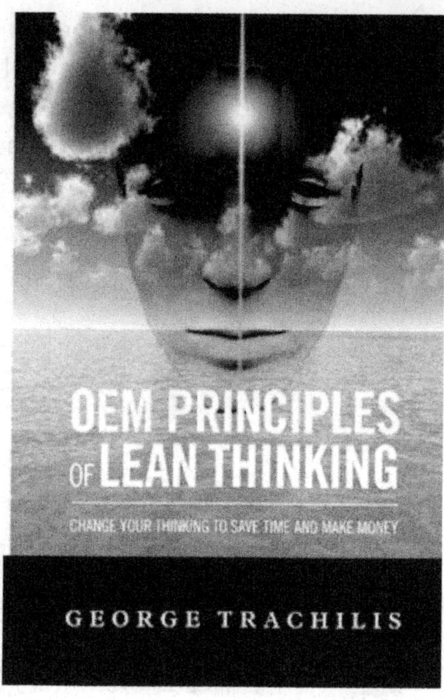

George makes his online course affordable for all future Lean Coaches by giving it away, Free. The hope is that those who learn by doing end up joining the Lean Leadership Institute as either coaches, consultants or life-long learners. (http://leanleadership.guru).

We are excited to launch this, the third book in the Lean Leadership Development series, *Standard Work is a Verb*, carefully and methodically developed by John Allwood with Bob Pentland. The Lean Leadership Development model is a 4-step process. At the core is the fundamental, living True North value within the organization. We have shown Toyota's values inside the diamond below. While reading this book, look for opportunities to coach and develop others using this insightful information shared by Mr. Allwood.

For those committed to self-development, this book provides some great insight between a learner and his or her coach. It has the distinction of being the most important book in this series. Without standards, there can be no improvement, so enjoy, do, and learn from Mr. Allwood and his coach, Mr. Pentland.

We hope your enjoy the book as much as we have. We also encourage you to find a coach to enhance and expedite your learning curve. Life is short. Get more information on John Allwood's website at http://standardworkisaverb.com

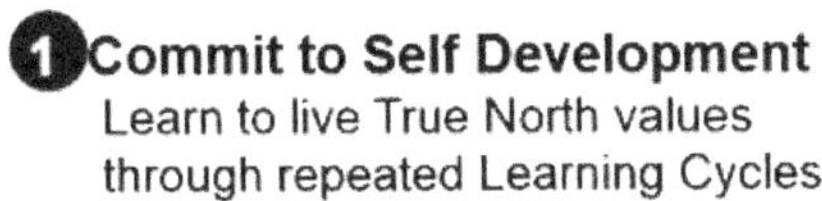
1 Commit to Self Development
Learn to live True North values through repeated Learning Cycles
TRUE NORTH VALUES
Challenge
Kaizen Mind
Go and See
Teamwork
Respect
2 Coach and Develop Others
See and challenge true potential in others though self-development learning cycles
3 Support Daily Kaizen
Build local capability throughout for daily Management & Kaizen
4 Create Vision and Align Goals
Create True North vision and align goals vertically and horizontally
P DO D CHECK C ACT

Lean Leadership
20
14
Institute Publications

Daniel J. Stanley
President, Lean Leadership Institute Publications
http://leanleadership.guru

FOREWORD

By Bob Pentland

I was blessed with learning Lean from, and implementing Lean with, disciples of T. Ohno. In the late 70's and early 80's, I was immersed in a rich environment at Jacobs Vehicle Equipment Company (Jake Brake). With the focused leadership of George Koenigsaecker, we became the first U.S. client of Shingujitsu. Prior to creating the consulting firm, they all worked for T. Ohno helping him to create and implement the Toyota Production System.

George and I became acquainted with one another prior to Jake Brake when we were in the driveline division of Rockwell International. With numerous trips to Japan and reading a difficult translation of S. Shingo, we began to "experiment" with Lean at our facility in Allegan, MI. George, understanding the commercial possibilities, quickly put us on a path of machining and assembling heavy truck drivelines one day in advance, and in line set order. Wow. Prior to this, we only supplied the components and the truck manufacturers did the assembly. They had component inventory up to their skylights. It was truly a win-win.

Subsequent to that, George became President of Jacobs Vehicle Equipment Company after a couple of years as the V.P. of Sales/Marketing. He quickly summoned me to come aboard and resume our Lean quest. Shortly thereafter, by a miraculous sequence of events (a story unto itself) we met and enticed Shingujitsu to come to America and help us. I do not use the word "immersed" lightly. We initiated Kaizen events at a frenzied, with multiple teams/topics per event. George was extremely predictive of their behavior. The more we were obedient to their direction, the more they taught us. No whimpering, no questioning, no indecision was tolerated. We complied. They taught by doing. We learned. Quickly, we started impacting non-financial metrics. Shortly thereafter, the financials improved dramatically.

Jake was one of fourteen lines of businesses within Danaher Corporation. Coincidentally the two Group Executives had their offices in our building. Soon the question was asked by them, "Will this 'stuff' work in any of our other businesses?" I truly did not know. George, in typical George fashion, responded "Absolutely!" As a result, in addition to our journey at Jake, George and I trained and facilitated Danaher Company-wide events every six weeks at all our locations. If you were a president or vice president of operations, and you wished to maintain those positions, you participated in these events. This became the foundation of the Danaher Business System (DBS).

For me, this was very fortuitous. Danaher was a collection of eclectic companies. Wherever we went, regardless of the product, the tools just worked. Document reality. Remove some obvious waste. Create some flow and linkage. Remove some more waste. Create Standard work Combination Sheets, Standard Work Sheets, Percent Load Charts, and the appropriate Visual Controls. Follow the reds dots.

After Jake Brake, and a short stop at Otis Elevator in Bloomington, IN, I went into consulting with a former Danaher colleague, Bill Moffitt, of Moffitt Associates. I was a sole proprietor. The experience at the various Danaher line of businesses gave me the confidence to make this move. The tools just worked!

It was early on in my consulting career that I met John Allwood. He was at an LOB (line of business) of Tuthill Corporation. John, from the very first event, was "attracted" to the tools of TPS. "Attracted." That is, John came with an open mind. With most clients they have prior "U.S." manufacturing experience and either want to defend what they "know" (or think they know), or, are continually comparing and contrasting the TPS to where they are. This consumes energy—energy that could help facilitate a Lean Journey. I have often wanted one of the "flashy doo devices" from *Men in Black.* My best clients were those that had already recognized what they knew would not work, or those with no manufacturing experience (high potentials gaining experience). John had prior manufacturing experience, and for whatever reason, chose to "check it at the door".

I experienced John's growth. It started with just asking questions. This progressed to questions about how to approach a specific opportunity. Then, he moved along to citing an opportunity and offering two or three alternatives of how to apply the tools. Then, it would be, "I had this opportunity, this is what I did. What do you think?" He developed a great appreciation for the Standard Work Combination Sheet. I was truly happy with his learning.

John then moved on to another job opportunity. This caused me some concern. At Tuthill there was a legitimate appreciation of the tools (specifically SW) and were supported from the very top. That environment is truly rare. Fortunately, in my consulting career, I was able to be highly selective and never entered a relationship that did not have the full commitment to the journey from the top leadership. John did not have that opportunity prospect. Yes, there are some folks in leadership that "say" they want to do Lean, and have NO CLUE what they are uttering.

John's new employment and a couple subsequent thereafter, opened my eyes to how much John had truly internalized the fundamentals of the TPS. I spoke of how I was fortunate at Danaher to facilitate events at the various lines of businesses, and thus gave me confidence to go into consulting. In consulting, I had clients in a wide variety of industries, products and services. This ranged from explosives to aerospace. I quickly became confident, and then comfortable, confronting unique, strange, even bizarre situations.

We stayed in weekly contact discussing the application of the tools. In addition, this brought to light an aspect of John that I had not been aware of previously. Regardless of what the new leadership said about "supporting lean," he always found himself to be a "salmon swimming upstream." In addition, he always found a way of "getting it done" (implementing lean). He was quick to access the dynamics (politics) of the leadership and "manage" them accordingly, while, creating fruitful relationships with the shop floor folks.

On this journey, I came to another new awareness. Several of John's new employers were suppliers to major U.S. manufacturers. These leading U.S. manufacturers all had their own "__________ Production System". As suppliers to them, John's employers were bound to comply with their direction to "do" lean (as opposed to "being" lean) adopting their "_________Production System." These OEMs would have their lean office equipped with their "black belts." Ironically, when these folks would complete their training for their suppliers, John would INEVITABLY ask, "What about Standard Work." They were always "put to confusion."

At Jake Brake, under the intense and comprehensive guidance of Shingujitsu (specifically Nakao and Iwata), I was quick to learn that "flow and linkage" generated immediate benefits (inventory reduction, improved quality, flow time, and others). With flow and linkage, I refer to these as "one time benies." SW (the Standard Work Combination Sheet, the Standard Work Sheet, and the Percent Load Chart) MUST support these. While "flow and linkage" provides "one time benies," SW, specifically the Standard Work Combination Sheet, is "the gift that keeps on giving." This manifests itself in the equation CT=TT (the time required for an operator to complete his/her tasks = the beat the rhythm of the customer). This is THE systemic equation for Continuous Improvement. Moreover, you never get there. You never get the CT to equal the TT. It is a journey. Toyota, after all this time, has not attained CT=TT. Toyota, being in the business of Continuous Improvement (not automobiles), is quite "happy" not attaining CT=TT.

Standard Work (specifically the SWCS) is THE foundation of the TPS (the true Lean). It amazes me how this has been lost. Perhaps it was never truly comprehended in the beginning. For those companies that might have had an "inkling," well, creating the rigorous environment to support it (CT=TT) was beyond the comprehension, let alone capability. As a result, Lean has been terribly diluted and misrepresented by most firms (consulting and manufacturing).

For example, commercially available, you can buy the 5-disc set on the 5S's, and derive many great benefits. An Olympic Event, unto itself. I was taught that the ONLY reason that the 5S's was to facilitate an operators ability to comply with the SWCS.

John has a comprehensive understanding of SW as the foundation of the TPS. He knows what it "looks and feels like" at traction on the shop floor. He also understands the relational dynamics in an organization that are required to allow it to flourish.

Leaving consulting I joined a client.

Bob Pentland

List of Illustrations

Chapter 3

Chapter 4

Chapter 5

Chapter 6

Chapter 7

Chapter 8

CHAPTER 1 - Prologue

Specific History and Origin of Concepts

Sometimes, the flavor of the journey is worth the price of admission. So it has been for LEAN and me. My journey began in 1997. LEAN came to Tuthill Pump in Alsip, Illinois just one day after I started as a manufacturing engineer. The new president of the company had been practicing LEAN in his previous life and he came to us equipped with a plan to change the company's operating system in a similar way.

We were introduced to the book, *LEAN THINKING* by Womack and Jones, which was widely circulated throughout the organization. The basic opening perception was that LEAN might cause folks to lose their jobs. There was curious discussion and even some light panic. I remember a few folks opting to leave rather than suffer this change even though nobody really knew what the change would look like, but you can bet it would be bad.

We soon started having company meetings to discuss the state of the company and the reason for change. Costs were beginning to approach incoming revenue. We had a huge warehouse full of inventory, but we could not make a shipment. The presentation(s) pointed out that the current accounting perspective was calculated on parts produced, even just to be put in inventory, and it had actually been causing overproducing of product that our customers didn't need (absorption accounting). It was one of the very first issues as a company that we were challenged to deal with.

Finally, we were introduced to the consultant. His name was Robert Pentland. Our new president pointed out that Mr. Pentland's LEAN story was a featured chapter in the same book that he had started us out with (*LEAN Thinking*). Indeed, there he was in chapter 7 called, "A Harder Case," which outlines the start of Mr. Pentland's LEAN journey, beginning with Jacob Vehicle Equipment Company ("Jake Brake") in Hartford Connecticut, 1987. Upon my further examining of the book (with renewed interest), it looked like Mr. Pentland had a direct connection with Taichi Ohno through the newly formed Shingijutsu Co Ltd (they were all former employees of Ohno). They were Mr. Ohno's original disciples and now, Mr. Pentland's teachers. Mr. Pentland appeared to be the only one in the book with that particular distinction; a connection, two-steps removed from the master's own hand. Two undeniable facts were established early on and they permeated daily life at Tuthill Pump: Our operating system was no longer working to the desired expectation and needed to be changed AND we would be following Mr. Pentland's LEAN guidance unflinchingly.

Mr. Pentland's training was complete and simple. I won't recount the basic principles of LEAN but they were all there (Takt Time; eight wastes; make value flow; etc.). It did not take long, though, before we started talking about documenting reality and writing Standard Work. We learned that the process goal was to create "The Least Waste Way" and that Standard Work was the tool used to support that. Mr. Pentland taught us that there is a direct connection to the customer through Standard Work as Takt Time is always kept in the forefront of writing Standard Work. In a recent conversation with Mr. Pentland, he strongly reminded me that the essence of this concept is as blunt as the following: Takt Time **(TT)** is the beat, the rhythm, of the Customer. When the SWCS (Standard Work Combination Sheet) supports the TT, your delivery performance (assuming the TT calculation was correct), will be 100% on time. Further, in supporting the customer, this formula, CT=TT, drives CI. It is the company's first real representation of a plan to satisfy the customer (or not).

The tools that Mr. Pentland taught for documenting reality and writing Standard Work were simple, concise and few. No alternatives were offered and no reinvention was ever tolerated.

By early 1998, we were in full-blown transformation mode. The overview training quickly lead to Kaizen type activity; structured, weeklong, team based events—initially to create flow and linkage. Invariably, the activities left in the wake of Kaizen were "Standard Work – centric." Standard Work was written to stand for the process created; Standard Work served as the production expectation which was to be worked to; Standard Work was at the center of "Real Time Problem Resolution" at the new cells; rewriting Standard Work was the objective evidence that continuous improvement had taken place and Standard Work was front and center in the visual controls. These activities served as the drivers of LEAN muscle memory development. They also became the drivers of culture shift (you know the one; it's the shift toward "that culture" that all authors seem to agree is necessary for REAL change to take place). The one main difference, as I can recall, it was that we didn't really talk about changing the culture so much as we executed on the list of tasks every day and over time, it became our culture. The "gotta wantta" to keep doing these things was never in question. The idea that the company WANTED to transform into a LEAN operating system (as trained by Mr. Pentland) was always in the forefront of all company communication and we never had dissention. The clarity and resolve of the company helped us focus energy on the tasks that drove the change. We were facilitating this change in a union shop, and we never had a problem with grievances. The Standard Work approach makes good and reasonable sense. It is an objective, observed work sequence actually performed by the process operator. As support folks and process operators worked together to establish Standard Work, ties and communication were strengthened. There was a refreshing energy present in all that was going on.

After about the first year of the journey, I was appointed "change agent," and I held on to that position for eight more years. It took several more years before I really understood what that term meant. The transformation at Tuthill went well and I had the chance to internalize all that Mr. Pentland taught us by teaching the others and practicing Standard Work in a LEAN biased environment. I knew no other "way" of LEAN—for years, and years. Shangri La! In addition, the tools—they always worked—even when we didn't know what we were going to find (in the next situation). Over the years, Mr. Pentland became "Bob" to me a dinner at a time, and our history is a blessing that I treasure.

What It Takes

Then came the time for me to move on (a story for a different book) and, just like on the shop floor, I did not know what I was going to find out there. In 2007, I set out for the great wide manufacturing frontier. Over the next several years, I found evidence of LEAN here and there. Often times I was too late, only to find that LEAN had been tried and was now taken off the post. I found LEAN in reinvented forms, often connecting the LEAN and Six Sigma disciplines. I found a lot of specific LEAN tool specialists, who were geared mostly towards supporting / promoting the tool that they were vested in like value stream mappers and 5S experts and Kanban-eers. I had been through small operations that had folks who claimed to be zealots and I had been through very large companies that claimed to be teachers of LEAN, but nowhere--NOWHERE--was there any physical Standard Work to be found—at least no standard work combination sheets, as I had learned to write Standard Work on. Nowhere. There were semi frequent discussions on the subject of "standardized work" (which is a term that shows up in books by Imai, Womack, and Liker), but those references seemed to have been written to compel industry leaders (with philosophical content mostly), but they are a little light on application specifics.

Not a single physical piece of Standard Work did I find; none that I hadn't written, anyway, for I kept writing Standard Work myself every chance I got. As a manufacturing engineer, I used Standard Work to problem solve, or as a driver for productivity. I wrote Standard Work to facilitate administrative operations. I wrote Standard Work to help in designing and estimating new processes. I have written literally hundreds of pieces of Standard Work since I left Tuthill, and the pattern of how I would approach problems on the shop floor using Standard Work became a sort of playbook that I would depend on. I came to trust that it would show me the way every time, just like in the good old days. Local results were consistent and predictable and I always exploited the chance to promote the LEAN message. Sustaining gains that had been made through the use of LEAN tools was typically poor due to a general lack of commitment to the ideal or connection between ownership/management and the shop floor.

The Good Sense of Standard Work

Talking to folks about Standard Work was yet another thing altogether. Those who were unfamiliar with it were usually afraid that writing Standard Work would be an insurmountable, mind-numbing task. I would hear that there were too many part numbers or that the process was excessively diverse. In such organizations that didn't have an established bias for LEAN, I would typically start by talking to process operators about what they do. Standard Work takes a specific interest in what process operators have to go through to make the process successful. It does so in an objective and fair-minded manner that shop floor folks seem to appreciate. It stands to reason that this makes sense to me as I ran machines myself for 20 years before I moved on into manufacturing engineering. I myself remember thinking that the managers had no idea what it really took to do the job I was doing. There seemed to be a three-sided disconnect between the design, the operations planning and the actual manufacture of the parts that I was running. I remember thinking, "If they could see how many times I have to handle" or "How many adjustments it takes . . ., they might decide to do things differently." Industrial engineers seemed more focused on the machine's times in those days, and after they did a "time study," they typically just returned a labor standard in the form of labor hours per piece. I had to do math just to find out what that meant in terms of how many parts per hour I am expected to generate. Time studies produce a work standard (a noun) but they do nothing to describe the work sequence required. The hands of the process operator are closer to the actual flow of value than any other hands in the organization. Documenting their work elements makes sense and the workforce will find it engaging and refreshing. I have never had problems talking with shop floor folks about LEAN tools. At the end of the day, LEAN serves everyone's best interest, and that includes the shop floor. When the labor standards that bidding work is based on are inflated for the sake of playing it safe, a company's ability to be commercially competitive is seriously at risk. To me, the worst part of the hedge fund that folks hide behind is based on assumptions of difficulty and risk without even a first attempt to document reality and deselect some waste instead of writing it into the Standard Work. The end result is the ability to command more work for the organization and to fill new capacity. I have never heard an employee say no to job security and this is the right kind.

My Own Journey Continues

Over the past year, I have had the opportunity to facilitate another true LEAN transformation with a company called PGI in Illinois that I had joined three years earlier (again, as a manufacturing engineer). We have been writing Standard Work and using it in various ways throughout the shop floor. At PGI, Standard Work is not only philosophical but also physical. You can find a Standard Work document next to where "Standard Work" is being performed. This company has also had to deal with what it takes to make a LEAN transformation and the role that Standard Work has to play in that. Recognition of the paradigms that have driven cyclical behavior exists and the company has made changes. The folks here have come to want for something different out of an operating system. They are able to remain curious and follow the tools to see where they show the way. Most importantly, the support staff is substituting time intensive former activities like sequestered meetings and closed door planning sessions with the new activities out on the shop floor as a means of finding the time to engage in them. At the end of the day, time on the shop floor is what it takes. You have decided you are interested in a LEAN journey, after all. Eventually, you have to go down to your shop floor. What are you going to do with your time out there and where will you find it?

Why This Book?

On my journey through the manufacturing hinterlands, I discovered that there are some strong challenges to the LEAN way. Some of the more classical arguments include LEAN vs. MRP; LEAN vs. standard cost accounting; Standard Work vs. standard work instructions; the shipping schedule vs. Pull. Finally yet importantly, the "where did you ever see that written?" usually referring to my description of Standard Work. Over a decade and a half had slipped under my feet on my LEAN journey and during one of my many dinners that I have enjoyed with my now good, close, personal friend, Bob, I happened to ask him if he might still have one of the original training documents that Shingijutsu came equipped with back in 1987. I had heard stories of this book through my training with Mr. Pentland in the Tuthill days. It was described as being "wafer thin" (the thickness of a sole on an Italian loafer) with just the few tools in it (time observation, standard work sheet, standard work combination sheet, percent load) that Pentland had originally taught us. He used to tell the story that Ohno would say that he could run the company with just the Standard Work documents that were presented in this thin manual. For me it would be the holy grail of LEAN artifacts. Bob's answer to the question of whether he still had it was, "Yeah, I gesso. It might be in my garage." After verbally beating him about the head and shoulders for never having shown it to me before (. . . a document that I have taken a stand for, many times to my own detriment . . . I'm done ranting now), he kindly agreed to produce it for my examination, and produce it he did. There it was in the pages of the first LEAN training manual to hit Western manufacturing (as far as I know or am concerned): Standard Work presented in the form of a standard work combination sheet **(SWCS)** and a standard work sheet **(SWS)**; objective time observation **(TO)** as the primary form of documenting reality; performing work to expectations to drive real time problem resolution; a few LEAN principles--all packed into 55 short pages titled, "How to Implement Kaizen in Manufacturing." All there. All true. A genuine LEAN artifact. Arguing those challenges that I listed first in this paragraph can be tricky enough for the average person navigating LEAN principles. Those arguments often serve as a defense of some sacred cow. I can certainly answer for where I have seen something written pertaining to Standard Work, though. Standard Work is a verb. It is a philosophy supported by specific activities as laid out in this manual, which contains Ohno's principles of application. It is very clear.

In my journey into the frontier of LEAN, I found that the information that I was trained on has not been widely communicated as evidenced by all the LEAN operating systems that have been extensively documented but are more than just a little light on the Standard Work end of things. I am a lover of LEAN Principles, but I am afraid that without a playbook to approach the shop floor with, the overarching principles fail to gain purchase and the once exciting and energy infused LEAN initiative withers and dies. I also think folks that are setting out on a new journey need something to do. Documenting reality through time observation and writing Standard Work is one stop shopping for creating connections between ownership / management and the shop floor and driving a new culture that is best suited for navigating a LEAN transformation. As such, my deepest fear would be that the message of Standard Work gets lost in the articulation of LEAN principles application approaches such that organizations that have the desire to start a journey, get mired in top heavy concepts and are never able to drill down through them to get down to the shop floor. I feel the main missing link is Standard Work (for most folks). I am writing this book to serve as a "stand" for Standard Work. In 2008, I wrote an essay to some LEAN leaders that stands as a manifesto of my beliefs in Standard Work and why I have them:

Dear Caterpillar Production System Leader,

I very much am enjoying the CPS for suppliers training journey and am very excited about CPS. I have been involved in just such a transformation from conventional batch and cue to a production system before. There were some differences and a lot of similarities, so I feel I know this rollout process (at least somewhat). I spent nearly ten years on a journey with Tuthill Corp. rolling out TBS (Tuthill Business System–7 years as the company's change agent). Our teacher's name was Bob Pentland. His teachers were Masaaki Imai (wrote the book, KAIZEN), Yoshiki Iwata, Chihiro Nakao, and Akira Takenaka; all of Shingijutsu Consulting Group. THEIR teacher whom they worked for was Taiichi Ohno, the cat that CREATED the Toyota production system. Womack features Mr. Pentland's journey with the disciples of Ohno on page 128 in the book LEAN Thinking and Jones in the chapter called, "A Harder Case." The path Mr. Pentland led us down was very much a LEAN program (only three steps removed from the master's own hand) and he taught the subject with great discipline and prejudice. He also taught us some problem solving techniques that I think borrow heavily from Six Sigma (although I did not know that at the time) but much more focus on real time problem resolution.

I am a great fan of American manufacturing (3rd generation, actually) but I have witnessed it dwindling in the face of Global competition, and that hurts me deeply. I am also, by the way, a big fan of CAT (in the same way that any kid likes dump trucks, diggers, and stuff like that- and the American manufacturing thing too, of course). With all that in mind, I feel that I have a deeply vested interest in the success of CPS, and it is with that in mind that I would like to comment on the program so far.

I think that CAT has pulled together all the right stuff to form CPS. I especially like the roll up of the 15 Guiding Principles into the three Sub Systems, and of course, I love the inclusion of the LEAN tool kit. I think the attention to the social implications (the cultural side and change management) is right on the mark.

I have one specific concern, also. I think that you might run into trouble with the CPS Standard Work program. I think it is a bit cumbersome and I fear that there might be issues with trying to get folks to write enough of it to really get a sufficient impact. Let me explain. Mr. Pentland taught us to write standard work within disciplined guidelines. He taught us that we can simulate or write the elements down proforma but after the first cycles; then you must engage in actual time observation and use the actual flow of performed elements to write a Standard Work Combination Sheet (SWCS). A Standard Work Sheet (SWS) must be written also and can contain enough detail to make clear the process, but more often than not a simple sketch of the work area with element numbers and path is sufficient. A good SWS will highlight quality checkpoints, safety concerns, and SWIP (as in inventory). The SWCS usually has enough space left on it to tape the SWS right on it as an inset. It is also a good idea to tape the actual time observation sheets on the back of the SWCS. The SWCS has safety and quality details marked on the margin next to the related elements and the SWS has room to show where standard work parts in process (SWIP) should be. All documents should be written in pencil, colors in ink or highlighter (for all the same reasons that are outlined on page 15 of your value stream mapping resource book, Learning to See). When it is done, just run the whole thing thru a 3-mil laminator, punch two holes in the top and post at the point where the work takes place. We settled on a C sized document for the SWCS and would order tablets of them to draw from.

The regimentation may seem a bit stiff, but, in fact, it is actually quite fluid and, I believe, that is how Ohno intended it to be. Let me explain. I think that Standard Work is the alter upon which Ohno laid his religion and that Ohno's LEAN supports all the same principles as CPS (safety, cultural change, visual management, bias for action, etc.) with Standard Work as the sun about which all those other things orbit. They receive their energy from Standard Work and their reason for being is to support Standard Work so that Standard Work can drive Continuous Improvement in real time on the shop floor where all the problems AND the answers are. I think that Ohno understood about the velocity of manufacturing, the problems and waste that get in the way, and the tools we use to manage manufacturing. All these things have velocity. If the tools we are trying to use are bloated and sluggish, their deployment and usage will lag behind the volume of problems that keep coming and the tool's effectiveness and fidelity will be compromised. The structure of Ohno's Standard Work makes it the highest velocity LEAN management tool there is to deploy and use. A time observation and Standard Work can be written by anyone and conceivably without even leaving the area of work. It doesn't require an engineer. It doesn't require a computer. It can be audited and updated by anyone who stops by the work area and reads along with the action being performed. It can be fixed with a razor, a pencil and tape. A revision is made official with a new date and another ride through the laminating machine, ready to be reposted. Do not waste your time trying to duplicate Standard Work information in routings or other electronic or hardcopy files. Of course, cycle times for accounting purposes or unwieldy technical data or information should still be kept electronically, but Standard Work can be one stop shopping for the granular detail on what happens in a process and one stop shopping for certification audits as well. The Standard Work Combination Sheet also shows the relationship between the operator and the machine cycle time, the operator and walking time, the operator and waiting time. Cycle times can be reduced by looking at what the SWCS is trying to say to you and rearranging elements to mitigate waiting (of the machine or the operator). Standard Work Combination Sheets posted in a work area are their own visual control; one dirty sheet on top of a bunch of clean ones = not using the Standard Work; lots of mark ups = somebody is loving and caring for the process; etc. Standard Work is also the best training tool there is. Anyone can give training by standing by and reading elements to the new guy. The following are comments made by Mr. Pentland himself to the content of this paragraph.

CT=TT=CI. So simple and yet so complex. There are very few folks, maybe 50 in the U.S. that truly understand it. Focusing on the shop floor, where maybe only 6% of the cost of goods sold resides, will in fact expose the other 94%. Really. No one understands this. It is hopeless. Then there are those that say they understand and want to "improve" on it. This is nonsense too.

My book will have two pages, CT=TT, and One Piece Flow. It will NOT be a best seller because it does not have glitz and so on. B. Pentland 9/15/08

If you haven't gathered by now, I am a Standard Work zealot. I do think that using a LEAN based production system IS the RIGHT THING TO DO. I am just being a stand for Standard Work and all I want to do is talk about it with anyone who will. I was in the right place at the right time to learn and do some cool things with Standard Work and I am willing and eager to share!

I hope you receive this message in the spirit it was intended, as a no strings gift from someone who genuinely cares about CAT and what your organization is trying to do. Good luck!

Sincerely, John Allwood
9/24/08

I was still seven years away from laying hands on the Shingijutsu training document, but Bob's training was true. Having seen the book only strengthens my resolve and belief that Standard Work, the Verb, is indeed the beating heart and the true driver of LEAN.

I have established provenance, connecting the material represented herein to Ohno as the architect of the Standard Work that I will describe in the pages of this book. I have practiced and applied Standard Work over many years and in many different situations so as to reinforce my resolve that it was at the center of the vision that Ohno had. I believe it is best put in one of J. Liker's books, *Deceptively Simple*. SO, as it pertains to the tools of Standard Work, how to use them, I will speak to them in this book as material facts, without offer of reinvention or an alternative.

That is my story and I'm sticking to it, as they say, but I present it as a direct witness to the material, and to how Bob Pentland presented it, and I present Bob as a material witness to the origin (with supporting documentation in publicized print). Those are simply facts. However, I also present my own journey of amazement and frustration as I have been exposed to many flavors of the LEAN offering and never encountered as sensible an approach as using Standard Work as the overall strategy from which to approach creating a LEAN operating system. I have received extensive training in "Six Sigma / lean; "LEAN-Sigma"; CAT CPS; and others, even earning green and black belt level certificates in them, and still, none of them had the connection through the tools and training down to the shop floor that Standard Work LEAN did for the years that we implemented it at Tuthill Pump. Nothing made the same sense to me and most of the others were so top heavy that actually getting through the training socializing to the business end of LEAN was always difficult at best. I always returned to what I had learned before the turn of the century and it has never failed me. So with all that having been said, and if you want to read about how LEAN was originally intended to be, and you want to make it work for you, read on.

CHAPTER 2 - LEAN Calibrated – The Goals

Creating a Value Delivery System

I spent most of my time at high school in the shop classes. It's not because I was too dumb for the college preparatory classes. If you would have asked me at the time, I might have said that I was just too worldly, so I did what came naturally to me. I went straight to work - adding value. For me, that meant that I took my shop class education and found a turret lathe to run (talk about worldly!). My introduction to the "real" world came in the form of a job in a small machine shop in Brookfield, Illinois. The conditions for getting paid went beyond just showing up. They only paid for parts that I ran; actually had changed the shape according to what a customer wanted. I can also remember the labor cards that we filled out at the end of each day actually had small print at the bottom of them that said, "We pay for good parts only." Just think about it for a second . . . a job that makes clear where the money you are working for comes from. It was life for me from the get go and I have come to appreciate the advantage that such a start would provide me in the longer run in terms of beginning to understand the notion of value.

The idea of considering where we are on the value adding scale is a loaded one, because everyone likes to think that they are doing an important job, or a "good" job or that they are appreciated for what they do; natural stuff, really. Most of the time, those tasks that folks must do to keep their jobs ARE important, if only for that reason, but it doesn't mean that the customer would ever specifically pay for any of it. So the **C** word rears its ugly head in the fundamental definition of value. That point of clarification (the customer's "willingness" to pay) helps me with objectivity, anyway. The customer wants something, made of some stuff, shaped to fit and function as the customer wants. AND the customer probably wants it at the exact time that they need it. Consider a product that is common with you as the customer, like a gallon of milk for instance. What you would pay for and what would cause you to walk away? I like milk. When I go into a store, my milk expectations include that it is fresh and healthy to drink; that I get every bit of the gallon that I am expecting; and that it comes with the bare minimum of packaging to keep the gallon together for the ride home and in my refrigerator for about four days. If any of these basic requirements went unmet, I would be disappointed. That seems like an easy one. Now, what about this scenario? I come in and I see that the milk manufacturer has started packaging their milk in stainless steel containers. They are really nice and silvery, and they add $8.50 to the cost per gallon. There may be value in that neat new container if it were able to keep milk fresh for a month, however, I already pointed out that I consume my gallon of milk in less than a week. Between my refrigerator and the existing packaging, less than a week is covered. There is no product value for me, the customer, in the new packaging. I walk. SO, our working definition of product value is raw material, which has been changed into a shape that the customer is willing to pay for when the customer wants it. Now we are making money!

Where does one go to find where that is happening in their operation? Go find the processes and the process operators. They are making the company money by creating the value (outlined above) that is paying the bills; specifically; literally. Adding value is not just a principle. You can go touch it. You can hang out nearby. You can observe and document it. You can support it by making sure the process operator has everything they need to be successful. And here's the beautiful part. Once you find it, turn around and take 10 steps in the opposite direction. You have just taken 10 steps away from value adding and closer to the lovely world of NON-value adding. Here is the punch line for all you captains of industry; if you aren't making money (adding actual value), YOU ARE SPENDING MONEY! Brutal, right? I love it.

By the way, just because there are process operators adding value somewhere in the operation doesn't mean that the company **is** efficiently delivering that value to the customer. It is very possible (and unfortunately endemic) to strand value in the form of unfinished piles (of parts) or excess inventory and as value languishes, it leaks away. The "if you aren't making money, you are spending money" adage works for parts, too. I have worked for business owners who over produced to the extent of having finished goods in their warehouse for years and years. The finished parts are carried on the books as assets and the expectation is that those parts are potentially worth every bit of what they were the day they were made. However, there is cost in carrying those parts (subtitled: All inventory is evil). The space they occupy is worth something. There is often a cost of carrying inventory at audit time. There is certainly a cost every time an employee has to move those parts around. We heat the parts in the winter. We keep them clean (maybe), or we spray them will oil mist so they won't rust relaxing in the extended stay parts hotel, and then we have to clean before we can use them again. In addition, we have to make silly transactions in SAP so we know how many we got and where they are, *AND THE REAL ISSUE IS THAT THIS INVENTORY IS A SHOCK ABSORBER, A RUBBER BAND. IT COMPENSATES FOR THINGS THAT GO*

WRONG. IT HIDES OPPORTUNITIES FOR IMPROVEMENT. Years later, when we sell them (if ever and at all) their original price doesn't begin to cover the ongoing cost of the existence they spent in inventory (again-evil). In LEAN terms, if you can create a "delivery system" designed to minimize the stranding of value on its way to the customer, then inventory is no longer necessary. Couldn't everybody do with less evil in their lives?

A value added delivery system is one designed to create and deliver value to the customer when they want it with the highest appropriate quality for the lowest possible cost. That rather describes the overarching goal of LEAN at maybe 50,000 ft. This description lacks application detail, but it is a place to start forming a perspective. At about 20,000 ft., you could say that the basic approach to creating such a system would be to make value flow and eliminate waste from the process. These are bolder, more action-specific statements and the excitement builds. I think one of the problems today in much of LEAN training is that the presenters have a problem with drilling down past this point. All this theory must have something to do behind it or making the connection between the principles of LEAN and what to do about it once (and oh my goodness, I hope you make it there) you get on your shop floor.

Standard Work – The Least Waste Way

Now that we are thinking "value delivery system," a suitable vehicle to create and support that structure will be required (and here's the good news); you can get from 20,000 ft. to ground zero with just two simple words: Standard Work. It is the GPS of value adding processes. Take driving a car, for instance. GPS is about providing a traveler with details (both visual and instructional) for traveling a complex path to get somewhere. It assumes certain base skills. GPS doesn't describe which direction to turn the ignition switch or how to put the car into gear. This is how Standard Work differs from work instructions and make no mistake, Standard Work doesn't endeavor to be a replacement for work instructions; however, I have seen processes fat with work instructions where various operators were still running the process in non-standard ways. For goodness sake, don't forget to train your operators to drive the car, but then you have to give them adequate travel directions if you expect them to arrive at the correct destination.

Standard Work comes from observing and documenting the processes where value is being added (where the money is being made). The elements observed are written in plain speak, not tech-eez and their firing order is established by witnessing the actual performance and the desired outcome. Then Standard Work is used to show opportunities for getting rid of waste and for showing how flow and linkage of formerly disconnected processes can be made. This is LEAN "rubber meeting the road" stuff here, folks. All other LEAN internalization exercises, classroom training sessions, informative power points and all other "what have you's" going on in LEAN training today are important to helping learn the framework, but the minute you go out and document process reality and write it into Standard Work, then you are working on a value delivery system already, and it counts, counts, counts (even in the form of practice).

Bob Pentland Writes:

"I learned from my teachers that Time Observation is truly the heart of Standard Work and not something to be done by the flunkies. In Japan in an event, Iwata asked me to observe a changeover. I went with clipboard and watch. Twenty elements in 10 minutes. As I started reading what I saw back to Iwata, he started saying, "Ah, very good Bob-san." I knew I was toast. When I was done, he proceeded to recite FROM MEMORY what he saw and the elemental times. He saw over 30 elements, remembered in their sequential order, and was asking questions as to their value to the process."

There is simply no down side to getting real with what is really going on in our processes. It IS where all the cash is, after all. There is much to learn from LEAN tools and internalization exercises. They are invaluable for getting the LEAN chops of a team up to speed, but until you go out to your shop floor and **document your process reality** so you can write it into Standard Work, then you haven't actually started working on a delivery system yet. Eventually, someone has to go out on the shop floor.

"I don't do time studies" is a battle cry that I often extol. The main reason for that is that time studies (of the traditional industrial engineer) return a work standard (a noun). One of the primary differences between work standards and Standard Work is that work standards are primarily focused on the output rate determined and never on the detail that the rate is based on. In my experience as a machinist (20 years, by the way), the work standard was just a number for me to try to hit and it typically wasn't sensitive to what I had to do, in what sequence I should do them, or the space I required. It was just a number to hit. Quite often, it didn't even come in a form I could use. The work standard usually was expressed in labor hours per piece. I had to do math to find out how many pieces per hour I was expected to make. As a machinist, I was aware that some of the operators had figured out little tricks or created special tools for themselves to help them make *OR BEAT THE RATES.* These "special" tools usually lived in their daddy's toolboxes. Other process details could also change over time, including the kinds of tools available on the market, if there had been an engineering change, if the company increased post processing or inspection as a countermeasure or a corrective action and "special" shortcuts might be used to overcome the change and maintain the operator's ability to make the rate. All these scenarios could happen but a work standard won't help expose the impact they could have on the customer. *Standard Work is so much more than a production rate.* For starters, it is based on a fair witnessing of the actual work sequence being performed; not simply the intention of a process as perceived by in engineer in an office 8 years ago or 43 miles from the shop floor. Perceptions *are always* vastly different from reality on the shop floor. In addition to getting clear on reality, Standard Work shows in a spatial way how the work flows and how the work area looked at the time of the observation when the Standard Work was established. It shows exactly how many Standard Work pieces in process is the least amount of inventory required to create flow **(SWIP)**. It identifies inspection points, safety points, and hand tools used (for the sake of 5S). Therefore, as things change, Standard Work should change as well. The minute that the Standard Work is suspect, there are only two choices: fix the sequence that has gone astray so that it fits the written Standard Work *OR DO ANOTHER TIME OBSERVATION AND REWRITE THE NEW STANDARD WORK!* That mantra works across the board. "I can't find the Standard Work." Rewrite the Standard Work. "The standard work combination sheet is too old to read." Rewrite the Standard Work. "I don't have that tool anymore." Rewrite the Standard Work.

Rewriting Standard Work should never be the act of blindly documenting a new and different string of activities to replace the old ones. Once Standard Work has been written, the opportunity exists in observing the operator trying to perform the Standard Work, cycle by cycle. I use the actual Standard Work Combination Sheet and keep time on the margin next to the element list. What I usually find is that most of the Standard Work elements hold up to within seconds and the real problems are local to just a couple of elements. Restoring the Standard Work or establishing the new "Least Waste Way," *WITH COUNTERMEASURES* is possible.

Standard Work defines a cycle time as the time it takes for an operator to perform all the tasks of an operation required to be successful and return to the start point. It may or may not include a machine cycle. Certain cost accounting perspectives and classical industrial engineering time studies focus on the machine or automated cycle times. Quite often, this perspective fails to account for piles of unfinished parts that are lying around and the waste that accumulates. The Standard Work Combination Sheet shows the "combination" of machine cycle and human elements required to support the machine and to finish the parts. The Standard Work Sheet shows the flow of those elements in the workspace. Cycle

Time is the time required for the operator to perform all the elements of the process, *OR THEIR PART OF IT,* and return to position of element #1, *TO START THE NEXT CYCLE.* If the cycle time (machine + human elements) supports Take Time, then "keeping up" with a machine cycle will not be as important as the human elements required to finish the work described in the Standard Work.

The very best part about writing Standard Work is that the activity is not limited to engineers or professional people or those who have a special, magical computer program. Anyone who has a pencil, paper, eyes and a modicum of training can do it. There is no technical limitation or software expense. It doesn't matter who has a computer or an AutoCAD seat and who doesn't. I have written functional (first draft) Standard Work documents on cocktail napkins (some of my best LEAN work has been done on cocktail napkins—story for another day). *For this very reason, the inclusion of operators in the writing of Standard Work is not only possible, but also highly desirable and there can be no faster track to local ownership of the process than if the process owner identifies with the Standard Work. The intention of Standard Work's pencil driven nature is that it is given to amending in real time with highly technical tools such as tape, scissors, and, of course, more pencil (you could even work crayons into it). Once the process change is known and verified, quite often a support person can fix the Standard Work document right at the process cell without disappearing into his office or turning on a computer.* I have seen "Standard Work" represented on beautiful colorful documents with printed elements and pictures and symbols, beautifully laminated, that took 2-3 teammates a couple of days to hammer out. What comes to mind is that the last thing anyone would want to do after such a production would be to cause the Standard Work to have to be rewritten. I have seen such (the document) become obsolete before it actually hit the work cell. For the most part, as I have walked through facilities that aspire to write highly developed, team produced "Standard Work" and I have generally found it difficult to locate any on the shop floor.

As observers and writers of Standard Work spend time **OBSERVING** and documenting processes, elements of waste will pop out so they can be eliminated. By this, I mean it will be plain to see the operator when he struggles, when he does redundant things, or if he has to walk somewhere to get something. That doesn't mean you have to bake it into the Standard Work you are writing. Fix it now and write the Standard Work without that element of waste AND, that is never your last chance to fix the process, though. *YOU HAVE THE OPPORTUNITY TO DO SO EVERY CYCLE until the end of time (biblical).* Feel free to banish more waste and then rewrite the Standard Work! I would say that I am being redundant except that I just like to hear myself say it, "Rewrite the Standard

Work." No downside. It is this mantra that delineates the ethereal notion of standardized work that is the requirement of baseline LEAN type thinking mentioned Imai's and Womack's books and being able to say, "We DO Standard Work, here! How do we know? Here is the document that was written. Here is where we changed it. Here is where we do the things that the document outlines (hint: all statements should be made without moving your feet AND NO DIGGING IN FILING CABINETS OR COMPUTERS ALLOWED).

When it engages local ownership and is born of co-creation, the Standard Work (SWCS and SWS) writing process is a tremendous culture shift driver. The writing process doesn't take much time and can be deployed the minute you are finished with it. The same can be said for a Standard Work initiative throughout an operation. There is no downside to starting this activity early. Be sure to obtain the right training on the use of the documents, which will not take long (1-2 hours) so you are off on the right foot. A small army of support folks, properly prepared with the skills and ability to discern value added elements from non-value added elements as just mentioned, could go into an operation with hundreds of part numbers and have an impact starting almost immediately just by doing time observations and writing Standard Work. Moreover, the Standard Work written can include a focus on safety that will be far more effective than a safety-auditing program. Incorporated into the Standard Work Combination Sheet and Standard Work Sheets, an operator AND an observer could tell, cycle by cycle where safety critical points occur in the process and what is done to keep the operator safe.

Writing Standard Work establishes a baseline, which is the term often bandied about in "standardized work" discussions. There is a deeper facet to Standard Work, though. Standard Work is best described as the "least waste way" that we currently know today to do work (implying the notion of CI). It not only gives you baseline, but also it gives waste visibility and speed to correction and implementation. Seems like the total package to me.

Make Cycle Time = Takt Time

This is a very deep, deep diving, "Standard Work – centric" principle of LEAN, and it really ought to show up in basic training; however, I don't believe that many LEAN folks are even aware of it, let alone its role in creating a powerful value added delivery system. **Making Cycle Time equal to Take Time is first and foremost about the customer**. **It is the true connection to 100% On Time Delivery while driving Continuous Improvement.** The idea at work here is to intentionally try to perform EACH CYCLE to the Standard Work and compare the results to see when something gets in the way of a successful performance of the cycle. If we can see it and fix it, the next cycle should be successful and the customer is supported.

So what if the cycle time is less than Takt time? Life is simply good? NOT ON YOUR LIFE! When a process is over resourced, the CT is less than the TT, waste creeps in and destroys it. The safety buffer of time is actually a pervasive root cause of slide back. It is important to focus on performing the cycle to each Takt Time. Actually, feel the process as it progresses about the cell. Every time something gets in the way of a successful completion because there is a problem, THAT IS WONDERFUL NEWS! It means we can fix something and actually get better at cycling this process. You show me a process that makes output expectations 100% consistently and I'll show you money that is being left on the table. I'll show you pervasive waste that is being worked around. In addition, I'll likely show you quality variation. Working to a known expectation will serve to support the cycling of our money making motor while preventing waste from creeping in during the process time available.

There is one hard pitfall to be aware of in establishing work to expectations on the shop floor. Process operators will assume that it is like old "work standards" situation where failure to make the rate carries punitive ramifications, an assumption likely established by former or current company behaviors that were more focused on the person instead of where focus belongs, on the process. That is why it is important to acknowledge past sins as past and fully communicate AND DEMONSTRATE how it is that these tools have much different intentions and potentials and are being used as such. So, make no mistake here; working to an established Standard Work based expectation is about driving waste out of the process and not about rolling up the Standard Work document and rapping the operator across the nose with it when they don't "make rate." The most effective proof of your new intentions will be when you show up on the shop floor and spend time with workers and your company's processes, asking about what got in the way and "prevented" the process operator from being able to perform the Standard Work smoothly and fixing those problems and the Standard Work there at the cell. Ask them how their process is "feeling." Is something missing? What could be better? Engage the process operators along these lines and they will start to believe.

Just to make things interesting, there will likely be one immediate benefit of performing tasks to Standard Work expectations. I have seen it happen many, MANY times. Output of the process might increase by anywhere from 8% to 20%. A strong discussion would point to "Hawthorne Effect" as the leading contributor to the gain, to which I see no down side. Hawthorne Effect gains are about the workforce working with increased focus and vigor due to the impression that management is paying more attention or somehow cares more about the process at hand. Does anyone else find that statement intrinsically alarming? If the Hawthorne Effect is an anomaly, then what does the workforce think most of the time (subtitled: what is ownership / management projecting to them)? I think there are other factors at work, which serve to contribute to this out-of-the-gate increase in output besides just Hawthorne. The process of establishing written Standard Work inspires cooperative ownership of the process (between operator and support person) and there is no downside to that. In addition, challenging the process with an expectation of output brings on real time problem resolution as waste is plainly seen. The presence of waste shows up in missed output goals and the "REAL TIME" opportunity to ask "WHY?" presents itself. As problems get fixed (even small problems that don't take huge technical skills to fix), process output increases in earnest as more of the time available is used for running process cycles instead of doing other things: more parts, more value, more money (so long as the customer wants to pay for them). REAL TIME PROBLEM RESOLUTION IS A STRONG VALIDATION WITH THE OPERATORS THAT REALLY DO CARE!

There are very strong socio-cultural benefits in setting up a work process with Standard Work and expectations. On the most basic level, much of what support people do in manufacturing (and that includes executive management) communicates a perception to process operators of how important the actual value adding work elements being performed in our value streams really are, which, if nobody shows up, is not much. I have worked in companies where more structure and protocol was created for meetings than for value stream processes. As I said before, we only make money with our value adding work elements. Do we really believe that? Have we done anything lately to demonstrate that we walk that talk or even understand it at a visceral level? Here is one way; show up on the shop floor. Your operators will be the first to know if you are truly committed and will also be more than pleasantly surprised if you follow through and spend time in front of the value adding processes that they are working on with them.

A LEAN Journey's Goal – To Transform

So embarking on a LEAN journey is what you want. There is a lot of information out there to start learning and many resources that are eager to help. Training is valuable and getting credible training to help get started is strongly advised. Just know that LEAN is a contact sport. LEAN requires change on the shop floor. LEAN takes activity and activity will take time. Where will this time come from? It is a perennial conundrum and one that ownership / management typically fail to deal with. The time spent in the operation on non-value added stuff, especially support people (who typically only do non-value added stuff by our definition here) is plentiful. Initially, choices must be made and if getting LEAN off the ground may mean that, a decision to spend time doing these activities will have to be made. Can't find enough expendable support people doing non-value added work to do time observations? What are you doing, Mr. President? Mr. Vice Pres. of Ops? Any number of overlord managers? Remember the assertion that if you take 10 steps away from the value stream, you are 10 steps too far away to be able to help! All the people I just listed are way further away than 10 steps. My teacher, Bob Pentland, as Vice President of Operations was required to take the lead on LEAN at Jacobs Brake in 1987. He was the one who first learned how to write Standard Work and he wrote a lot of it in the beginning for his company's existence. A LEAN transformation is not something that you send your minions out to take care of. The moment a time factor (or lack thereof) discussion comes into play; I would start recruiting from the top down. May as well engage your MOST non-value added employees out of the gate (not a slam – reality). That fact is that the payoff towards the LEAN transformation by having top executives engaged just as much as support staff will have immeasurable impact on the culture of the company on a couple different levels. For starters, ownership / management are not exempt from benefitting from paradigm breaking and re-education in the ways of LEAN. It's a tough lesson to learn about value: what is and what isn't. But taking such a lesson to the shop floor and showing the workforce the highest level of commitment to an ideal that has never been demonstrated in the company will infuse the workforce, and the support staff with energy and resolve. This isn't a flavor of the month or just another initiative and the workforce will know it.

The other source of time will come from eliminating waste. All waste has a direct association with people time. Overproduction: someone had to run a machine longer than they had to. Traveling: someone had to move stuff from here to there. Hand-offs (over processing): More hands than necessary. The elimination of any of these wastes free up people power, and the golden opportunity would be to engage in an activity that achieves this in a real way so that you could redeploy folks to work on LEAN things – *redeploy - NOT LAYOFF.* This final achievement is like a boulder rolling downhill. If you can get this one going, it will build speed, power and excitement. It will change the way people think about how things used to be done in processes and what is possible if you spend enough time to get intentional with your processes. Remember, this is a transformation. I love Webster's definition as applies to math: "The operation of changing one configuration or expression into another . . . a change of variables or coordinates in which a function of new variables or coordinates is substituted for the original." This really describes LEAN transformation to me, at a depth that transformation would be real, comprehensive and lasting, as opposed to a little bit of this, and a little bit of that. A colleague once described this kind of dabbling as "Mambo #5" LEAN (reference the song). It makes for better music than as an approach to implementing change.

A strong word of caution from Bob Pentland:

"WITH REGARD TO NOT LAYING OFF PEOPLE, COMPANIES THAT EMBARK ON A LEGITIMATE LEAN JOURNEY WILL NEED TO GROW THE BUSINESS (SELL MORE) TO ABSORB THE PRODUCTIVITY."

'Nuff said?

Now let's learn how to work these documents and apply these wonderful tools!

CHAPTER 3 - The Standard Work Tools and Skills

So, You're Still Reading! Wonderful!

Congratulations. You won't be disappointed by your decision to focus on the work elements of your processes to expose the massive amounts of juicy, fat waste, and the precious actual lean, value added elements. The tools and skills outlined in this chapter will wind up being your go-to approach to getting acquainted with the processes in your own operation, and I say that very deliberately because everyone I have ever traveled this path with, or alongside, has said the same thing, "I had no idea we did all that?" Alternatively, "Is that really what it takes to make one of those?" They had really never gone out to spend very much time around the work being done by the workforce. If you are anything like me, you will come to love these tools. They appeal to me on so many levels. I never feel so connected to the operators and where the value of the operation is created as after I have spent the time to watch and document what they did. I always love to watch their faces as they realize that I have gleaned an actual sense of the order of criticality or complexity of their process by simply watching what they did.

Learning how to work with the tools is not very hard in reality. The forms are actually very easy to learn and we'll get right down to that in a moment. Internalizing the essential power of the tools is where things get interesting; learning how to see the value being created and learning to see the waste that strips the cash away from any value created and how pervasively waste creeps in. Example: Ask a forklift driver to drive your parts all around the facility and you will pay him for doing it before any financial statement can tell you if you made money on the job or not. After you have written a couple of pieces of Standard Work, it is my prediction for you that elements of waste that you see will become increasingly frustrating and that waiting on the usual quality meeting or corrective action meeting to make the change becomes untenable. For me, writing Standard Work starts to satisfy my urge not to wait. Many times I have gone out and done a Time Observation and written Standard Work when I didn't really know what else to do (even if "write the Standard Work" wasn't the obvious answer, *which it so often is)*. In times like those, I have found myself looking back over and over at what I observed, and if the problem is a process-based one, those answers come out through the documented tasks list of granular detail. It will open your mind. Now, let's learn about the tools.

Time Observation – The Heart of Standard Work

Time Observation is where it starts. It is also the most demanding part of the whole deal and that is mostly because many people have convinced themselves that they are simply too busy to stand still and watch. Time Observation dictates that the observer stay with the process for as long as it takes to complete enough cycles to understand the process, with a mind for seeing waste and a desire to do the observation right. Many LEAN presentations and training modules that I have lived through talked all about the techniques that folks can use to obtain information about their processes. Such approaches include using video equipment; interviewing the process operator; presenting a process operator with a paper so they can document for us "a day in the life" (of that operator). These things make me crazy in that they are usually presented without another option; to go watch and document in person / in real time. All those techniques mentioned previously create excuses for not going out to the shop floor and spending the same time that our money spends swirling around in our processes. (You'll probably spend way less time than your money really does down there- swirling, I mean). There is no substitute for an up close and personal witnessing of each element in turn and each occurrence as it happens. Real time appraisal of what is being seen for relative value / waste will happen and the opportunity exists to write a corresponding comment. All those alternative techniques listed above on how to document reality lack the actual witnessing of reality, and that includes the videotape, which circumvents the opportunity to be in tune with the feel of the process. The video does nobody any good until someone watches it anyway. Time Observation not only accomplishes that but it results in a document that one could refer back to over and over, looking for details. In the world in which I learned LEAN, if the facts of a process didn't come from a Time Observation, then the credibility of their actual existence was in question, and at the very least, the cycle time or assumption that the process was really complete was always suspect.

Time Observation is the most important skill in the whole world of LEAN. I have gotten clear on issues that escaped anyone's ability to detect through productivity or effectivity report quotients. It is one of my favorite activities to engage in on the shop floor. I find it quite cathartic when the insanity of non-value added work gets to me; one too many meetings; circulating a report that no one reads; etc. Going out to see what somebody is actually doing—someone that is paying the bills (around here) is a good experience. One major thing that strikes me as wonderful is that process operators are almost always accommodating (if not pleasantly surprised to see someone show up). They genuinely love to share what is going on with someone who is willing to hang out and see what it takes. I am also never disappointed at how much insight they have into what is wrong and what they routinely have to do to compensate for things that haven't gotten fixed and how willing to share that information they are with folks that are genuinely there to help.

Time Observation requires practice. If it feels funny at first, just stick with it, it gets better. It requires several iterations to become competent. There are situations where observing and documenting the process seems easy and clean. The operator has a real sense of order about how the tasks are performed. There are other times where it seems like the operator is doing a random string of activities and writing them down seems like a losing proposition. With practice and a little relative experience, the observer will learn what is going on (as it pertains to the skill of observing) and how to deal with it. For example: If you have gone out to the shop floor to document a process that was recently put in place and you are going to establish the baseline cycle time, but every task string of elements is different from the last, and things get in the way of the process in each cycle, then this process may not be robust enough to do a Time Observation and write the Standard Work. Steps towards stabilizing the process should be taken before any thoughts of writing the Standard Work are entertained. Fix the process. I have seen more Six Sigma folks stymied in their attempts to collect data points to plot because the process lacked basic stability and intention. Variation in the actual tasks translated into variation in the actual outcome. That doesn't make for good box and whisker charting. Go fix the process, or (in as many cases as I have seen) create a process with intention. You can start by going out and standing with your hands in your pockets to see if the process is repetitive. If the operator is doing things randomly, kindly ask him to do the process one way. Once there is repetitiveness, the elements can be written down.

So, just go out and practice observing. There is no downside. There is a downside to writing Standard Work before it is ready to be written (with all the initial waste baked in) but there is ABSOLUTELY NO DOWNSIDE to observing and documenting a process in your plant. Go do it. And do it again. And do it again. At this stage, it bears mentioning that it is important to consider the verbiage to use for the elements as you are planning to list them on the Time Observation Form and the Standard Work Combination Sheet. Knowing that the verbiage on the SWCS comes from the TO form, focusing initially on the words is the first step to exposing waste. For instance, the urge to observe an operator 'procure a drill from somewhere, drill four holes and put the drill down' and write, "Drill 4 holes" totally misses the "go get" part, which sounds like opportunity to me. Instead, elements listed as "go get the drill"; "drill 4 holes" separates the value added from the opportunity clearly and the decision to change "go get" to "pick up" by way of repositioning the home of that drill permanently can be made, and Viola! Real Time Problem Resolution and Least Waste Way Standard Work! Along those same lines, as you are learning to observe the operator, is the question of whether he LOOKS comfortable performing the process or can you SEE HIM STRUGGLING? If you think he is struggling, chances are that he actually is. Practice this skill of observation first before concerning yourself with marking down time. It helps one get right with the notion that Time Observation is not done just as a productivity tool, although it certainly does have a profound impact on productivity in the longer run. It will never be enough to simply collect the results of performing to the expectation. The goal is to perform each cycle to the expectation. A concurrent goal is to perform each cycle safely and Observation and writing Standard Work will have a similar "right off the line" improvement in safety in a real way (real results – real reductions in occurrences). All details with respect to EPA; OSHA; and other safety-based considerations of personal and environmental safety are much better executed according to Standard Work.

There are a few simple rules of engagement for performing an effective Time Observation:

1. First and foremost, do not stage the activity you are going to observe (unless, of course, it is a new process and a Kaizen team is trying to establish flow). It is very tempting to come in and chat up the process operator to the point where he is no longer performing the tasks in his natural order. *Avoid the impulse to interview him* and if he starts to explain a lot of what he is doing as he is going along, make clear that it would be best for him not to do that.

2. Write down what the operator is doing, IN PLAIN OLD DIRTY ENGLISH (not IE'ese or whatever the native tongue happens to be). It is about the operator and how he/she is interacting with the process. IT IS NOT ABOUT THE PART OR THE EQUIPMENT, THE MACHINE, WHATEVER.

3. The most desirable observation is an objective one. Just observe. Sounds easy, right? Not! Objective observation is a learned act to be practiced. As a manufacturing engineer, I was (am) guilty of making running identifications and appraisals of problems/issues/opportunities that I found myself in front of. Occasionally, I would be making up my mind as to what was happening before arriving at the scene of the problem. I

sometimes even had a preconceived notion of what I wanted to do about it before I got there. This may sound ridiculous but it really happens (no hate mail, all you engineers!). A great way to train away from this problem is to observe processes that are very unfamiliar. No knowledge of the process is required and in many cases the less the better. Watch carefully and pick out the value being created and the waste involved in the process. Try to understand if the operator seems comfortable with the process or if he seems to be working to overcome impediments, and make comments on the form describing what you see. When you are done, share what you saw with the process operator including the relationship you observed between the machine cycle and all the things the operator does as he works around it. If you have done well, the process operator will be impressed at the level of understanding you have gained through your observation.

4. Once the stopwatch has started, it is not to be stopped until the end of the observation. A profound difference between classical time studies and Time Observation is that in time studies, the watch is started and stopped constantly in order to get elemental times. *The problem is that time leaks away if we're not careful to document none value added opportunities.* When the stopwatch never stops, non-value added elements are exposed for what they are and the only two choices are to write it into the Standard Work or get rid of it immediately so you can write the Standard Work with less waste.

5. Finally, don't forget to relax. I have had Time Observation students get very nervous and flustered once the signal to proceed was given. Don't be afraid to try. Start out on something simple just to get the hang of it. Write the work elements down first, once they are repetitive. Then start the stopwatch and mark the times. The last column on the right, "points observed" is a very important one. What was seen that caused the variation? If Time Observation doesn't come naturally at first, that's OK. Just stick with it and the task will come easier in short order.

Time Observation takes an investment of premium resource time. It is not an assignment for filler folks, temporary workers, flunkies, or summer interns (what are all those things, anyway?). The first people on the field of Time Observation valor should be the company's leadership. This is for two very good reasons. First, as important as I have articulated this skill to be, so must the leadership desire to master it. I had a plant manager who did one and he was done. Poser. If you don't believe it Mr. Manager, neither will your folks. Two: you should be the teachers to your folks, not me (if you want to gain real traction, that is).

Bob Pentland remembers in the late 80's:

"I finally came to appreciate that my teachers, every time that they were on the shop floor were doing real time multiple TO's. That is as they were "JUST" walking through the shop. For EVERY operator they saw, they were assigning elemental verbiage, and constructing real time percent load charts in their heads. That is why on an initial visit to a potential client after touring the shop floor they would say, "You have 50% too many people?" They meant it and were correct!" (B. Pentland '16)

Enough of all that. It is time to get acquainted with the documents that we are going to discuss in this chapter. They include:

- Time Observation Sheet
- Standard Work Combination Sheet
- Standard Work Sheet

They pander to the lowest common denominator and that is not referring to intellect. That is referring to equipment. If you have a pencil and form, eyes and a time reference, and the curious mind to want to SEE the process in a way you never have before, then you can use these tools. They are not computer or software dependent; they are not education / degree dependent; NO EXCUSES. All are created equal in the eyes of Time Observation and Standard Work. The only limitation is that those who never do can never fully understand.

PROCESS OBSERVED:		TIME OBSERVATION FORM		DATE:		OPERATION NO:		PAGE
				TIME:		OBSERVER(S):		OF
STEP	TASK DESCRIPTION (Describe what the operator does in everyday language.)	1	2	3	4	5	TASK TIME	POINTS OBSERVED
	TIME FOR ONE CYCLE							MACHINE CYCLE TIME(S):

Figure 3-1: Blank Time Observation Sheet

What you see above is the actual Time Observation Form that Bob introduced us to in 1998 (see figure 3-1). It has survived in my files through the magic of photocopy, and while a few of my colleagues have reliably and faithfully recreated it in other programs so as to be able to save and share it electronically, I have always come back to this one. I just like how it feels, like a very well broken in baseball glove to me. No other one is required. Let's take a quick look at what is on there.

For starters, notice that there is a whole title block on the top. It serves a couple of purposes. For one, I would like to think that after reading this book, people are going to start to do so many time observations in their manufacturing operations that it would be handy to keep track of what was being observed and the title block certainly would serve that end, so take the time to fill that stuff in. Another function that the title block on this (and on the SWCS and SWS as well) serves is as an identifier of original document. My administrative duties over the years have included the fostering of the LEAN component through ISO and TS certification processes. I have been through this very exercise at no less than three different facilities. The various examiners that I have worked with loved the hand drawn, and signed nature of LEAN documents because they are automatically "original documents" as opposed to "uncontrolled documents," and as such, kosher in the eyes of the cert doctors. So, fill in your title blocks.

The two columns to the far left (underneath the title block) are the "step" and "task description" columns. Those will be where the work elements observed (and in the order in which they were observed) will be recorded. It will take just a little practice to get the hang of deciding "what" an element is and by that, I simply mean how much stuff / how much time should be included in an element? The true punchline is that granular detail is always more helpful than broad-brush detail. In terms of time, I was trained to shoot for elements to be 6 – 10 seconds long. That would be the ultimate goal; however, there can also be reasons to be practical. If granular detail does not add value to the task at hand, then don't commit to over processing. For instance, an observation is going along well and suddenly, the operator takes off towards the inspection lab to search for a lost gauge. As the flurry of hide and seek activity unfolds, identification of a great big steaming pile of waste should be quickly made with resolve and without stopping the watch, granularly detailed elements of how the waste was conducted might be replaced by a chunky slice of time and lots of comments about fixing this part of the process before the Time Observation can be continued.

"Bob (in a whining tone after getting beat up three times for his elements being too large), how small do you want the elements to be?"

"Dave (now the president CEO of a 4 billion dollar company), how good do you want to be?" (B. Pentland from his Jake Brake days)

Notice the columns (with the cells split horizontally) labeled 1 – 5. This is where the running time is recorded and how the elemental time is determined. When the watch starts at 0 and the running time of each element is recorded in the bottom of the split cells (at the **end** of each respective element), then the elemental time can be calculated by subtracting the one you are quantifying from the one before it. There are devices and software that attempt to automate the calculating. With a very little practice, it is actually much faster to just use the documents and a pencil.

The final column is the Points Observed column. It is there to record comments, which associate to the element in the row. A comment could explain one inordinately long element of five (dropped tool) or why this is one great big element (hunting for replacement for broken tool). These comments become important clues and cues as to what was happening at the time of the observation. Often times, observations are processed on a subsequent day from when it was recorded and a little more detail helps keep things straight.

There are two kinds of Time Observations: Observations of repetitive robust processes, and observations of a single opportunity (such as a setup or a very long cycle). We will deal with the repetitive process first. When trying to establish the Standard Work for a repetitive process, I was trained to do an observation on 5 cycles, hence the 1 – 5 columns. From that, a very reliable idea of elemental cycle time can be determined (the technique of deciding which time we will discuss later – note the Task Time column). Transitioning from one cycle to the next should be done without stopping the stopwatch either. After all, that really is how our processes actually run: against continuous time, (the most precious commodity and one we can never recover).

In fact, a decent Time Observation is like a pencil drawn video. It is a running credible record of integrity as to what was happening at the time of the observation. I have conducted little informal tests with newer Time Observation students in which we documented a process and when we were finished I would start them talking about it on the way back up to the training room, but without referring to the document. Just like the old grapevine game, it was always surprising to everyone, how much their perceptions of what had just happened had changed in just the time it took to walk up from the shop floor.

Standard Work Combination Sheet and Standard Work Sheet

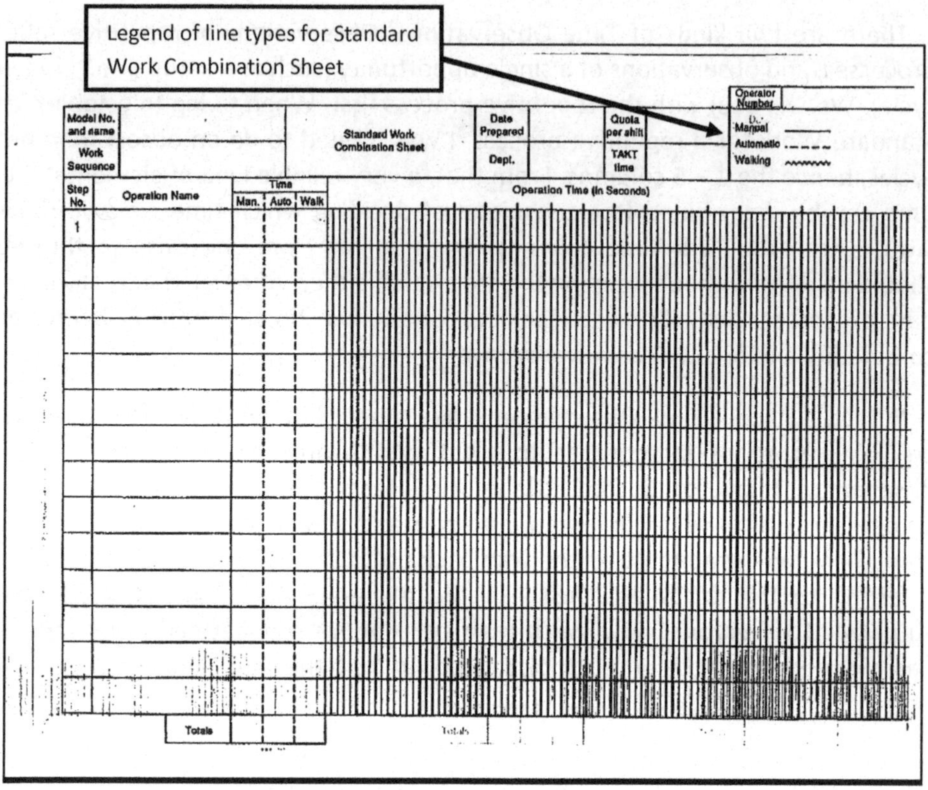

Legend of line types for Standard Work Combination Sheet

Model No. and name		Standard Work Combination Sheet	Date Prepared		Quota per shift		Operator Number	
Work Sequence			Dept.		TAKT time		Manual / Automatic / Walking	

Step No.	Operation Name	Time: Man.	Time: Auto	Time: Walk	Operation Time (in Seconds)
1					
	Totals				

Figure 3-2: Blank Standard Work Combination Sheet

The Standard Work Combination Sheet (see figure 3-2) is a document that can show the time relationship(s) between manual (human) elements and machine cycle times. This is the document that proves by illustration the principle that cycle time is ALL the elements to complete a process and NOT JUST A MACHINE CYCLE TIME; not unless you like to see an operator with nothing to do but sit and wait on a machine while making piles of stranded value. Even the operators don't like to do that (makes the day drag by).

This form has a similar title block as the observation form and should be filled out as well. Notice that there are a couple of columns on the left side of the page; the first one for element numbers, next for element descriptions (brief), and then three narrow columns for element times / machine cycle times / and time to WALK to the next element. They correspond with the observation (minus, possibly, anything that was observed as wasted and removed/eliminated).

The field to the right of the elements lists is portioned out in vertical lines to be able to determine a time scale, which will fit on the document that will contain the cycle time of the process. These vertical lines are grouped in fives to help with this. The time scale is noted and worked out at the top of this field (as I will illustrate below).

There are only a couple of different kinds of lines allowed to be drawn on the SWCS. They include a heavy horizontal one for human elements, a heavy dashed one for machine cycle, a double headed red arrow one for when the operator is waiting, a thin wavy one for when the operator is walking, and finally, one thin vertical transition line to show when elements are linked together without a time lag (no walking). When they are arrayed on the SWCS, they lay out like a Gantt chart for lack of a better description. For all you who are already firing up your Microsoft Project programs (tm), forget it. It is not the same thing. There are many beneficial aspects to writing Standard Work that you will lose by trying to use a computer program to write for you. I am not going to defend right now, so hold your questions, please.

The SWCS is the document that handles all time related information; element times, overall cycle times, Takt Time. Takt Time can show up as just a comment or as an actual red line that depicts a target for each cycle time to hit, but there are problems directly translating that in a mixed model environment, so I am going to handle that discussion separately. At this point, it is just very important to understand that all cycles have a direct, calculable relationship to the Takt Time of the customer.

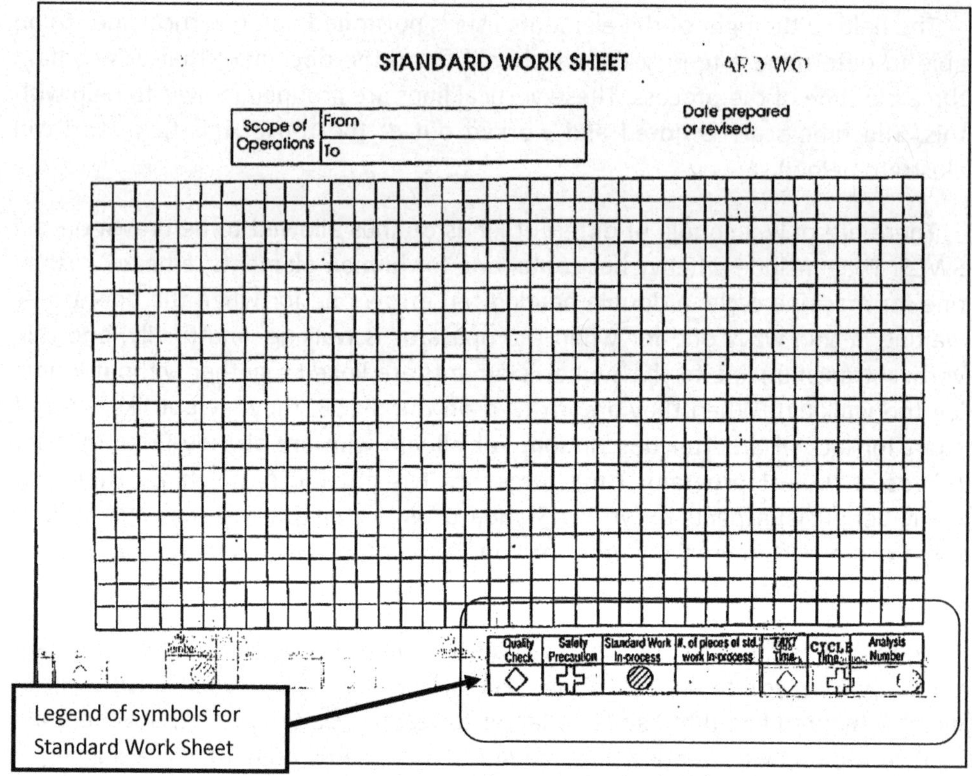

Figure 3-3: Blank Standard Work Sheet

The Standard Work Sheet (see figure 3-3) always goes along with the Standard Work Combination Sheet. It gives the spacial information of the process, starting with a simple bird's eye view of the work space and how the process operator moves around in it, step by step (correlating to those elements on the SWCS). This document looks like a piece of graph paper, more than anything else does. Label it with the same information in the title blocks as the SWCS so they are always a set. The rest is a sketch. Here is a hint: if it takes you more than 10 minutes to complete the sketch of the work area, you are over processing. It will still have more credibility than the facility CAD drawing. (You know the one; that the engineers drew three years ago).

There are a couple of symbols that are used on the SWS. One is a symbol for Standard Work in Process. This might be a new concept for some folks (If you are thinking "WIP" right now, this is new). SWIP are the parts left to run in machines as the operator unloads, loads, and cycle starts. It is the minimum amount of inventory required to run the intended process. The symbol looks like a horizontal oval with diagonal lines through it.

Another symbol that is used on the SWS is a Red Cross. It shows *where* safety is critical and what the operator should do to keep safe through Standard Work elements order, putting on PPE, or the use of equipment (like a hoist). Taking your safety program to the Standard Work will have a huge impact on incidents reduction. *The inclusion of the red cross does NOT preclude guarding, interlocks, and so on.*

A third symbol that is used on the SWS is a horizontal diamond shape. This shape is used to show where in process validations take place (the "what" is being done is covered on the SWCS). Remember: If you can't tell that parts are good or bad at the end of the process, then you haven't created Standard Work.

The final symbols used on the SWS are the circles with the corresponding element numbers from the SWCS. There is typically one circle for each element but if a number of elements happen in succession in the same place, a circle with a "number thru number" is acceptable.

The only "lines" drawn on the Standard Work Sheet are the lines that connect the element circles in order of execution, the process "path" with a dotted line that connects the last element back to the first. It is not a cycle until we are ready to begin again. On the SWCS, we must return to the first element as well, normally a "walk" line. The Standard Work Sheet does make a frequent appearance in non-Standard Work-centric LEAN training as the ever-popular "Spaghetti Map." The spaghetti map generally depicts the "before" state of a process and serves a very valuable service done in conjunction with the TO form in this regard but it remains much more powerful as the "other" half of Standard Work.

So the three components of Standard Work include Time Observation (the verb): both witnessed and documented with real time appraisal; The Standard Work Combination Sheet (the verb): translating the observation elements into time relationships, or "real-lationships" (see what I did there!) and completing the form; The Standard Work Sheet (the verb): spacial work space witnessing and the work elements relationship within, and completing the form with safety and quality foremost. I guess Standard Work really IS a verb! At this point, those of you who are wondering if your organization has "standardized work" or anything that comes close, can you find any of the stuff written about above in terms of either activity or documentation? No? You don't have it. You don't do it (Standard Work).

Writing Standard Work - Basics

Let's take a simple Time Observation through to the writing of Standard Work on a mechanical level. For starters, we will deal with a stable repetitive process. That makes the exercise really fairly simple and sensible. You see, the complexity of writing Standard Work is not buried in the working of the documents. I can teach anyone to use these documents much faster that they could learn MS Project. The complexity comes in as what you think serves as Standard Work, and right now, I am referring to your processes. Send a good fella in to observe and write Standard Work and find him stymied? I bet you don't have a stable enough process. What you have is an expert at work (your operator) and he is doing all he can to maintain and overcome the variation.

PROCESS OBSERVED: MACHINE & ASSEMBLE 123	TIME OBSERVATION FORM	DATE:	OPERATION NO:	PAGE
		TIME:	OBSERVER(S):	OF

STEP	TASK DESCRIPTION (Describe what the operator does in everyday language.)	1	2	3	4	5	TASK TIME	POINTS OBSERVED
1	OPEN DOOR - UNLOAD - BLOW OFF - LOAD - CYCLE START	14 14	15 100	12 185	14 271	13 357	14	MACHINE CYCLE < 50 sec
2	PUT ON PRESS SHIELD - USE DEBUR TOOL TO DEBUR I.D. - SHIELD OFF	7 21	6 106	6 191	8 279	6 363	6	SAFETY
3	CHECK O.D.	8 29	7 113	6 197	8 287	7 370	8	
4	CHECK I.D.	9 38	8 121	8 205	6 293	8 378	8	
5	CHECK THREADS	14 52	16 137	15 220	18 311	16 394	16	
6	P.U. PLUG & WRENCH	5 57	6 143	6 226	4 315	6 400	6	
7	INSTALL PLUG INTO PART	14 71	16 159	15 241	14 329	16 416	15	
8	PUT ASSEMBLY INTO PROTECTIVE SLEEVE - PUT IN BOX	10 81	9 168	10 251	11 340	11 427	10	
9	WALK BACK TO START	4 85	5 173	6 257	4 344	5 432	5	
	TIME FOR ONE CYCLE	85	88	84	87	88	88	MACHINE CYCLE TIME(S):

Figure 3-4: Time Observation Example

This is a typical observation of a short stable machining and assembly process that is taking place in my plant right now (see figure 3-4).

The process is a very stable one that we have written Standard Work for recently. We were able to establish the elements list by watching the operator before we ever started the stopwatch. Starting things out this way can help with the problem of deciding what is an element, what should it include and what should be considered as part of the next element. For instance, in the elements above where the operator is checking the features of the part, and doing so within 10 seconds, we decided that an element included picking up the gauge, using it and putting it back down *because those gauges were already at point of use.* It doesn't, by the way, include an adjustment or countermeasure for if the part is found to be no good. That should be left to produce a "red dot". A red dot is an *opportunity* to fix something and get better at doing it. Much more on this as time goes on.

Notice the zero just above the first split screen column. That is where the stopwatch was started. The running time then progressed down the column in the lower half of the cell splits. You can see the 14, 21, 29, 38 and so on down to 85 seconds, then the cycle started over and my next time entry was the 100 in the bottom split of the second column down to 173, up to 185 and down to 257; up and down the fourth and fifth columns down to 432 seconds and the completion of five cycles.

The resultant elemental times were calculated by subtracting the time in the lower halves of the splits from the ones before them.

5	CHECK THREADS	14 52	16 137	15 220	18 311	16 394	16	
6	P.U. PLUG & WRENCH	5 57	6 143	6 226	4 315	6 400	6	

Figure 3-5: T.O. Elements 5 & 6

See the time columns of elements 5 and 6 (see figure 3-5). Each of line 6's elemental times came from; 57 – 52 = 5; 143 – 137 = 6; 226 – 220 = 6 and so on.

9	WALK BACK TO START	4 85	5 173	6 257	4 344	5 432	5	
	TIME FOR ONE CYCLE	85	88	84	87	88	88	MACHINE CYCLE TIME(S):

Figure 3-6: Observed Total Cycle Times

This calculation pattern works on the totals line as well. Line 9 completes the process and so the time of the first cycle was 85" (see figure 3-6). The cycle time for the second cycle was 173 – 85 = 88".

Determining what the representative elemental time for the Standard Work Combination Sheet has been the subject of some very passionate discussions in my experience and after it all, what I have to say about it is don't over think it and don't let the issue become distracting. Once upon a time, we were trained to look for the "lowest repeatable" element time to put in the final task time column. The argument was that if you could do the element more than once, it wasn't an anomaly and, in the name of driving out waste, use that number as the Standard Work element time. The other camp (usually the one that has been answering for productivity measures) likes to point out that if an element might occasionally take a little longer, using a time that would encompass all element time variations (of course we are talking about very minor variations) makes life good (productivity wise). One can see how tricky this conversation can quickly become. My strong recommendation is that this issue be held up against the idea that a LEAN journey (any journey) has cadence to it. I consider cadence in this case to be practical, sustainable speed of application. That cadence is directly affected by such factors as leadership's resolve, problem solving strengths, commercial fluctuations and the socio-cultural climate (most importantly of all but made of the other parts). Without compromising on the principles of LEAN, Standard Work has to somewhat match whatever cadence the company is at or the LEAN journey can be hampered or impaired. There is much more to discuss on this point later in the book. Right now, we must get back to the elemental times in our example. The times that were selected were based on a reasonable observation of a stable time that will generate a healthy number of red dot opportunities to fix things. Notice that none of the times varied by more than 1-2 seconds and could have been considered human error with the stopwatch. If an element had included some nonstandard situation causing the element to be several times that of all the others, consideration of what happened and how to fix it should be made and then that particular elemental time excluded from the array. In actual observed cycle times 88" happened twice and 87" once. 88" is a reliable cycle time. The cycle also happened once in 85" and again in 84". The real question would be what are you prepared to do to go after the extra 3" per cycle? If you have to run 100,000 of these cycles, then the investment might match the result. If this is Standard Work for the 75 of these you make per year, then you decide how good do you want or need to be. As I said before, there will be more discussion on this later.

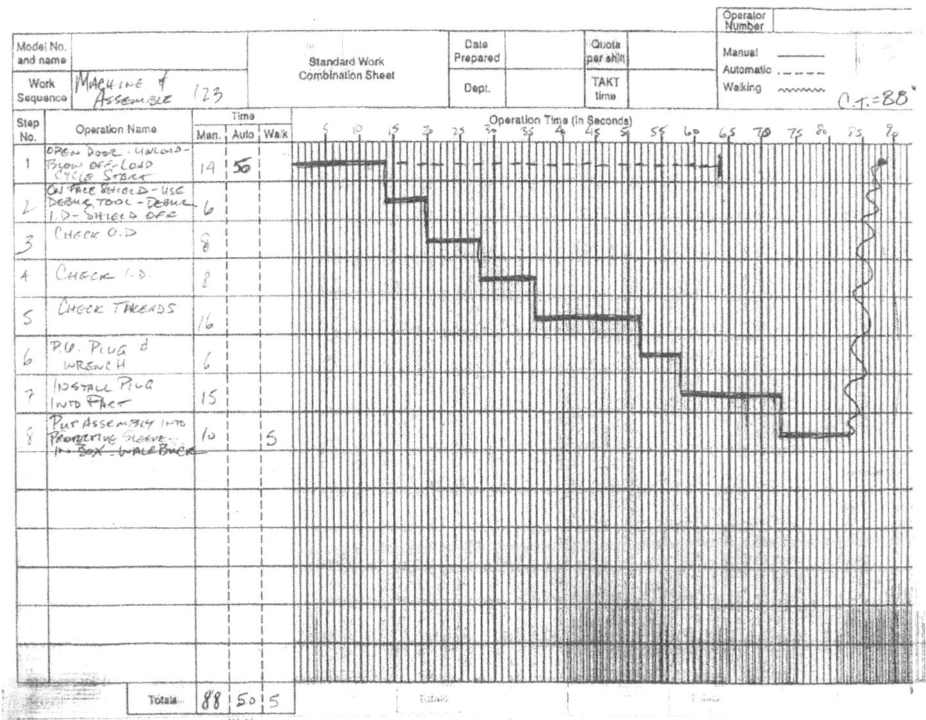

Model No. and name:
Work Sequence: MACHINE & ASSEMBLE 123
Standard Work Combination Sheet
Date Prepared:
Dept.:
Quota per shift:
TAKT time:
Operator Number:
Manual ———
Automatic - - - -
Walking ~~~~
C.T.=88"

Step No.	Operation Name	Time: Man.	Auto	Walk
1	OPEN DOOR - UNLOAD - BLOW OFF - LOAD CYCLE START	14	56	
2	ON FACE SHIELD - USE DEBUR TOOL - DEBUR I.D - SHIELD OFF	6		
3	CHECK O.D	8		
4	CHECK I.D.	8		
5	CHECK THREADS	16		
6	P.U. PLUG & WRENCH	6		
7	INSTALL PLUG INTO PART	15		
8	PUT ASSEMBLY INTO PROTECTIVE SLEEVE - IN BOX - WALK BACK	10		5
	Totals	88	50	5

Operation Time (in Seconds): 5 10 15 20 25 30 35 40 45 50 55 60 65 70 75 80 85 90

Figure 3-7: SWCS Example

Pictured above are the Standard Work Combination Sheet (see figure 3-7) and below, the Standard Work Sheet (see figure 3-8) that represent the written Standard Work for the observation under discussion. Notice that the same list of elements has been transcribed in the first column and the elemental times selected for each appear right next to the element. The box that is split next to element 1 was done to include the discreet machine cycle time for this process. Notice that this process cycle contains a machine cycle, but is not the equivalent to the machine cycle. The operator has been given more tasks to do to completely finish the part and assembly (This arrangement eliminates 3-4 process hand-offs). The overhead time line has been portioned to equal 100" so as to be able to contain the 88" of our cycle. Under the timeline, each manual element has a horizontal bar drawn to that element's time increment. In this case, each manual element flows into the next and the thin vertical line connecting them up to the last wiggly line, which indicates the 5 seconds it took the operator to return to the start position, depicts that. It is good to be diligent in including the "return to start" walking element is there to remind us that the process is most durable and services the customer best if we execute it again and again without pause. In addition, walking is waste and including all the walking that you actually see the operator doing in the course of their process is an opportunity to get faster and more efficient by eliminating the need to walk. The machine cycle starts at the end of element 1 and is 50" long. It goes out to the 64" mark and has a little vertical "stopper" to show that it is done. In this case, the machine is waiting for the operator. It was decided that the machine cycle time was far less than the Takt Time, so it was a better investment to engage the operator in completing the flow of the process than just standing there keeping a machine running *AND OVER PRODUCING (TO LOOK GOOD FOR ABSORPTION ACCOUNTING). Thus creating a better flow!*

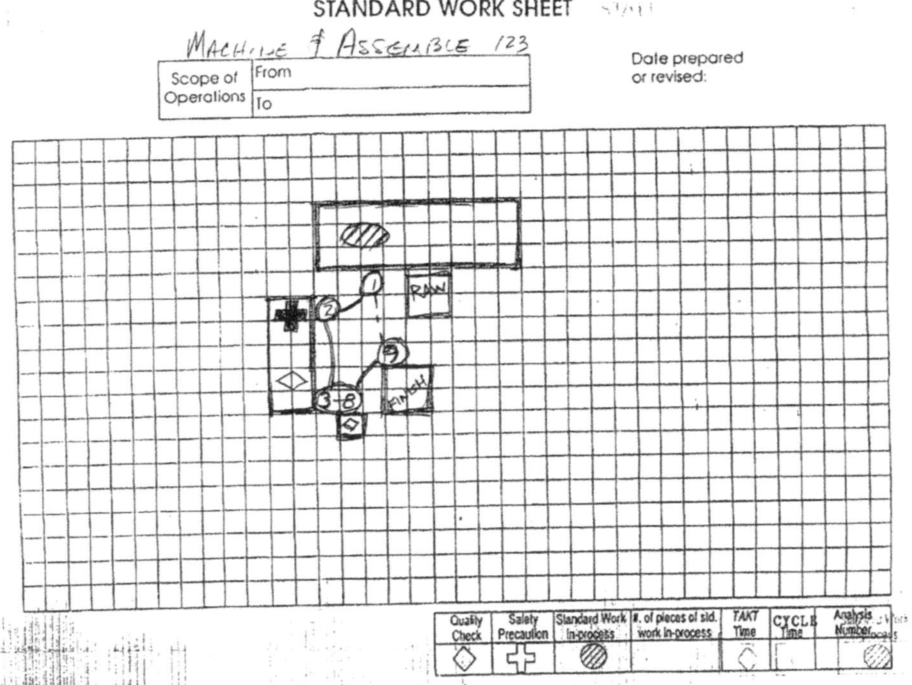

Figure 3-8: SWS Example

The Standard Work Sheet shows the machine with the "SWIP" part in the machine. That part is running while the operator continues through the process. The element numbers in the circles show where the operator is. There is a safety cross next to element two; the deburring, which indicates a safety concern and its countermeasure. The diamond shapes occur wherever inspection of a quality measure takes place. The first diamond is where the features were checked and there is one over element 8 where the finished part is put into a protective sleeve for shipping. The dotted line is concurrent with the walking element from the Standard Work Combination Sheet.

Time Observation and Standard Work for Non-Repetitive Observations like Set-ups (Start-up notes)

The above example of a documented process that has been written into Standard Work was a very simple one. Things are not always this neat. Many processes take much longer than 88" to execute and some processes are highly manual and could vary by just the manner in which a process operator picks up the part. Set ups are a process that inherently have approach variation based on what job was running last, and the opportunity to observe often comes as a one shot deal, not a "best of five" affair like in the example process. There is a Standard Work way to deal with each of these situations. They all involve using the tools just as presented here. For instance, observing a set-up is no more complicated than making sure you have enough forms and uninterrupted time to stay with the process. The observer will be using only the first column of split boxes to record the running elemental times as there is only one viewing of the process. The critical factor is to just keep writing and keep the stopwatch moving. Remember that a lot of things can happen in a minute so fight the urge to just let the stop watch run. Note the time down as the last moment of the element and start to write another.

When we first started learning about Standard Work and we started writing for set-ups, the term "horse blanket" was coined by an associate of mine. The illustration of his comment was the resultant large (three d sized pages taped together) piece of Standard Work that would inherently impractical to refer to and didn't really address that notion that there may be actual circumstantial variation in the process (like set-ups "from to") anyway. There is one very important awareness to maintain through any long-term (time) observation like a set-up. That is even if the whole process seems like a random order of elements, there will exist within small ordered groups of elements that can be identified. Often times, these smaller strings of elements are, in fact, very robust (process wise). These "component" parts of the Standard Work can be written as such and the reality of the Standard Work (for set-up in this case) becomes the array of which components are necessary for the set-up this time. Despite the apparent randomness of set-up, it is always made up of predictable portions of work. Even the cycle time of the coming set-up can be accurately predicted by laying out the portions of the "all up" Standard Work required. Similar techniques can be used to write Standard Work that is sometimes done by one operator and sometimes done by two. It can be used to write Standard Work for three operators working at a time across two shifts. The important part to realize is that while the application might feel a bit different, the specific use of the tools is just the same. In fact, I have written Standard Work for all of these situations and really did not know how I was to do it going in. I just followed the tools and the Standard Work popped out!

Organizing a Time Observation into written Standard Work can sometimes involve some creative ways of using or arraying the tools and I will get into some of that later in the book. For now, it is most important to practice using TO, SWCS and SWS to develop and internalize the muscle memory of them. It is also, at this point, important that the company's leadership find a way to truly embrace the activity for what it is: the new order of things as it pertains to the LEAN journey. All conversations pertaining to the process, to operations, to problem solving, and to business management should take place around this new campfire. If your CEO comes down to the shop floor, walks past the Standard Work and tunes in to the "Earned Hours Report", then you are still in trouble.

CHAPTER 4 - Higher Level Standard Work Talk

#1 Principle of Standard Work: It is a VERB

Now that we have laid a little groundwork with the tools, it is time to take a deeper dive on some of the "what it takes" side of getting the most out of Standard Work; making it meaningful; making the connection with the socio-cultural climate of the organization. And finally, creating a state of readiness for the culture to change to the ways of LEAN and Standard Work. There is plenty of material out there to help with change management. Change management shows up as a common component in LEAN coaching books, which I find comforting from the standpoint that LEAN is being presented with the idea that organizations are facing a comprehensive change from their current operating system to the LEAN Operating System, as it pertains to a "LEAN journey." It is important not to assume that change will happen without struggle or it will just happen automatically. Operating management cannot assume that they can call for change and then let the shop floor work it out. Whole careers revolve around the science and management of the very change required to transform to the LEAN operating system. I would recommend that anyone about to embark on a change journey explore some of the change management material available out there. I won't cover much of it here (except the occasional comment). Managing the change is imperative. The tools of the Toyota Production System simply work. That point does not require debate. The primary question is whether or not the ownership / management in your organization can create an environment that will let the tools flourish!

Future State Behaviors and Future State Beliefs

There is a component to change that I think is reflected in the values that support Standard Work as an activity. Standard Work is not a "to do" to just get through and check off the list. It is ongoing in every way, every minute of every day. It is the entry level of understanding and improving a process. The journey never ends.

Bob, *"Toyota has been trying to get CT=TT for 60 years. They just cannot get there, and, THEY LOVE IT.!"*

It is the way through to linking value-creating activities. It is the second, third, fourth, fifth generation of continuous improvement of the process. It is the stability of the percent load representing the customer. Standard Work is all these things at multiple stages of the above iterations throughout the LEAN enterprise- but only if there is a full complement of behaviors to support all the ETERNAL goodness available to the diligent. Without the action to back up the above, it is only rhetoric. There is only the promise of abject failure without doing the work. Practicing Future State Behaviors creates sustainable Future State Beliefs.

A Case for Action and the "Gotta Want It"

This would be a good time to check in with your company's expectations for your LEAN journey. All companies need a "case for action", a case for change. The indicators must be exposed and out in the open. Are you not meeting the demand or expectations of your customer? Do you have bottlenecks to break? Are you drowning in inventory and other cost / waste? Are you hoping for total salvation? These questions all point to the many symptoms that result from wasteful processing and could differ from operation to operation. Folks get excited as they imagine what their companies could look like without some of that mire. However, I always like to warn that any success, even lukewarm, fractured, or dysfunctional success is the natural enemy of change. As obvious as the need to fix the companies problems are ("when you say it that way") it is all the easier to fall back on behaviors that seemed to work in the past rather than risk more chaos in trying to change. Therefore, as I said, the change indicators had better be understood by all and acknowledgement that the desired state is something decidedly different than occurs in the present; in terms of the outcome; in terms of what behavior are currently performed to support. It is a simple model to imagine. The company's Case for Action must engage the company's specific desire to be different than it was a year ago, a month ago, a week ago. The Case for Action must engage the company's specific belief that the best the old ways of doing things can get us is lukewarm at best and lukewarm is death.

Fixing Things Makes More Time to Fix Things

While there might be enough energy to get started on a LEAN journey supplied by the aforementioned list, the really important follow up question is, "Where does the company expect to get all the manpower energy required for the change?" "Future State Behaviors" drive that little angle: that is, ONGOING activities that support the new order getting done- FOREVER! In the case of Standard Work, I am talking about taking a process-biased view of working on the shop floor and favoring time out with the operators over time in a meeting; as a matter of prevailing company values. If the motivation for getting these new activities done doesn't come from the internalized WANTS of the company driven by its strategic direction plan, then rounding people up for time observations will be like pulling teeth. Everyone will feel too busy to get out and do that. The key, as an organization is to be prepared to choose differently those things necessary to run the business and as you learn more about LEAN, those things that are perceived as being necessary to run the business will change. People aren't required to babysit inventory where inventory has been eliminated or put to point of use. Folks don't have to show up with a forklift where material no longer requires handling or moving. The banishment of waste frees up human time to work on the process, and I'm not just talking about direct labor time. The more waste gets driven out of the process and the more visual the process is made, the more capable the local operators become at managing the coming and going of material; become the drivers of "Stop to Fix"; the presentation to the customer. All this serves to free up the time of support folks for *real time problem solving.* That is high horsepower time, right there. That is a key level of talent to get convinced that the new activities out on the shop floor, the Standard Work supporting activities, are the right ones to pursue. *These folks are often times harder to get to turn from their former behaviors because they are used to surviving by them.*

Future State Behaviors

To be clear, by "behaviors", I am referring to the physical "what I do to get my job done" behaviors. That may entail, printing a report and then counting parts at all junctures. Maybe that means you get on the system and check for material availability. On the other hand, maybe you log in and then it's off to the production meeting for the next hour and a half (if you're lucky). There are the behaviors associated with problem solving or nonconformance investigation. In the old environment (at least in some of mine), investigating a nonconformance would be done from a corrective action meeting and inspection documents would be traced back to find out who did the work. *In the new future state, those same questions would be driven back to the process and the Standard Work.* Instead of going to the meeting, a group displaying new future state behaviors will sooner be drawn to the work area. Instead of pouring over reports and past tense circumstantial evidence, a group might elect to observe the process in action to see how it would be possible to make bad parts and to fix it so it can't happen in process anymore. There should be a developed and fostered bias for the later kind of activity that is located around where the action is and involves directly the process and those engaged in it. In my experiences, the former process tended to lead to the operator, or more specifically, is designed to seek out the operator with all assumptions, appraisals, and judgments in tow. I have seen organizations take the results of this approach and resolve to attempt to train operators to adapt and overcome out of control processes in a conscientious way (an oxymoron if you ask me), before even getting to the processes to see why performing them flawlessly is never possible. The resolve to seek out the Standard Work and conduct all Continuous Improvement discussions around that campfire is the new future state behavior. An organization cannot just apply lip service to that, an organization is going to have to physically practice DOING THAT in order to internalize and make it a habit. In so doing, the goodness of Standard Work will come out.

Future State Beliefs

So practicing future state behaviors will serve to form the future state beliefs that support the LEAN journey, which is driven by Standard Work. This is in alignment with and buttressed by the Standard Motive of the company to WANT to be better and WANT to do that by eliminating waste through Standard Work. This serves to form a Standard Response and (hopefully) becomes the Standard Attitude of the organization towards the processes, problem solving, and Continuous Improvement. Standard Work + Standard Motive + Standard Response = Standard Attitude. Once a group of folks can start to align the components discussed above, the "who and how much time should we spend" questions become a no brainer to answer. Who = everybody available; and how much time = ALL OF IT!

Bob notes:

SWCS has the TT line = OTD (customer satisfaction), labor (cost), quality, safety, SWS = inventory (operating working capital), safety, quality. WHAT MORE IS NECESSARY. Chihiro Nakao (O.G. Shingijutsu Sensei; ref: "LEAN Thinking"), "Bob San, only two documents required to run factory" (SWCS and SWS).

As I think more and more about the activities surrounding Standard Work, it becomes clear that those activities set in motion "real time problem resolution" or the old "Stop to Fix" battle cry. Stop to Fix is a LEAN principle that has strong roots in the standard motive-response-attitude idea laid out above, but without having those standard attitudes firmly ingrained, stopping anything to fix it in too many production environments is conventionally counter-intuitive. "Making the shipment/month," rules way too many roosts out there. Bob used to tell us (and he would preface with, *"Be careful how I say this"*) "I don't care about ***<u>that</u>*** shipment. I care about ***<u>ALL</u>*** the shipments". I think what he was trying to say is that engaging in the future state behaviors is painful at first but they lead to something better at a global level, not just a local level. Therefore, we have to engage in the practice of performing new future state behaviors.

Get to Practicing

What might some future state behaviors look like for those who don't have something immediately in mind? I can tell you what to start with. Do you perform any tasks worthy of writing Standard Work for? I bet you do! I am currently serving as an Advanced Manufacturing Engineer, which means I calculate tool path, and tooling costs for quoting new business for my company. The other engineers here think that "Advanced" is synonymous to "special" in the sense that I should have my mittens sewn to my sleeves, but really, I do quoting (which I could never do with mittens on) in advance of the engineers in the shop working on it (get it; "advanced" manufacturing engineer?). We have an expectation of lead-time to respond to the customer that impacts how long I have to do my job. In my case, we decided that I need to return a RFQ (with committed costs) in 20 working days. That lead-time is largely dictated by elements out of our control like seeking material and fixture quotes on the outside. However, it became clear to us a couple of years ago that our contemporary customers were asking for quotes much sooner than that. Therefore, we devised a quote process that covers all the elements that we control and figured out how to do it in 5 working days- then I wrote the Standard Work for it. I perform to the expectation and track my performance to it. Granted, a great deal of my process is administrative, but that doesn't mean that there aren't actual tasks that I perform in deliberate sequence and on a time basis. In fact, each time I execute my job, I have performed a cycle and each time I perform the cycle, I have an opportunity to ask why whenever something gets in the way and fix it. Moreover, rewrite the Standard Work.

An individual could write Standard Work for any task or duty; process or administrative. Then, go to the trouble of posting the Standard Work that they wrote right there where they perform the task. Keep the documents current and create a visual control (more on this in subsequent chapters) to indicate when the cycle doesn't go as planned so it can be fixed. Doing these activities will more than get a body started with internalizing Standard Work activities and establishing Future State Behaviors.

Internalizing the Future State

Here is another idea to help build Future State Beliefs. Find a task to do in service of the shop floor and create Standard Work around that. I was looking for just such a task to help promote Future State Behaviors during a LEAN journey where I work now. After a really valuable maintenance technician left the company and it became clear that ownership / management was not going to replace him, I decided that I would fill a mop bucket with floor wash solution and walk around the shop to help some of the operators keep some of the leaks in their machines clean. I knew that they were strapped and just could not get to their mops every day, so I just wanted to help. At first, my new activity was sort of random but I very quickly identified a time of day that I could typically be spared, which turned out to be 7:00am every morning. SOOOoooo . . . I hit the floor by 7:00 am and toured with my mop and bucket. Several wonderful things happened as a result of my daily tour. A message of a renewed value towards cleanliness by ownership / management was communicated through the workforce and they responded by upping their efforts to keep their areas cleaner (by choice, not mandate). Operators regularly shared ideas with me about problems that they deal with in their areas. I came to realize that I could affect "Total Productive Maintenance" more with a mop and bucket than any PM schedule alone can. Other good things happened over the couple of months that I initially started to sustain the behavior and I wrote the basic Standard Work for what I was doing every day. Then, something dawned on us during a discussion of safety; the only metric that we paid attention to was a days since last lost time accident board, which (thankfully) was into four digits. That really just means nobody cut anything off or was maimed (again, grateful), but the score was so perennially good that it didn't drive safety. We found that we really had not even a basic safety program. I took a look at the Standard Work I had written and was able to make safety related elements to be performed: Every day it is assured that any fluid hazard between or within 48" of all the yellow aisles lines is cleaned up and any trip hazard, wood, debris larger than a couple of wooden matches is picked up. When viewed from that perspective, it became this company's first proactive safety program defined by Standard Work and monitored by a very clever visual control. I do this mop tour every day. It does take up about 5-7% of my total time available, but ownership / management know exactly how much resource is going into the program (how long via the Standard Work) and they know just what result can be expected from the process (how safety effective via the Standard Work). The owner has decided to place a high value in driving safety and cleanliness (very wisely), so my 5-7% is worth the time and I make it happen. It has been nearly a year since I started the original mop tour, six months since I rewrote the Standard Work from the safety perspective and I maintain a visual control. I am sort of my own choir that I preach to, but I did learn several very important things in the course of sustaining this Future State Behavior (noted above) to internalize. By the way, none of the shop floor employees question my resolve in the new order or my ability to do what I say I am going to do and hold to it. I have developed a trust with them and credibility for what I am trying to accomplish there on the shop floor and in the organization at large.

"High powered executives may not relate to this example." **Warns Bob.**

My good friend has much more experience working to convince the powerful folks in charge to take the LEAN journey. In my journey, I have more often showed up in the middle of a LEAN shop floor mess that was typically the creation of insufficient commitment; organizations that never showed up to do the work-organization that never actually endeavored to establish and sustain Future State Behaviors to support the LEAN class room / book concepts. Bob's comment inspires me to say something here. I think the manufacturing world must enter a new era of LEAN understanding if LEAN is to survive. I do believe that in the beginning, it was very important to appeal to the captains of industry to take up the mantle of the LEAN message and as such, the message had to be tailored to the folks that Bob is referring to above, however, I never read anything that led me to believe Ohno said one could run their company by remote control or from the board room. I have read where Ohno's climb through the ranks of Toyota was actually impeded by his belief to the contrary. So mine is a simple message, if you are so high on the corporate ladder that you can't imagine having personal contact to the process floor, spending actual time as a function of your new Future State Behaviors for the sake of your LEAN journey, then you better be able to imagine that someone else, in fact a whole layer of folks, just below you, ACTUALLY WILL have time to show up, make contact, do the work as an ongoing specific requirement of establishing Future State Behaviors.

So there it is! See? Not so hard to find creative ways to work in service of the processes. It can be very cathartic as well, but mostly, it will help create Future State Beliefs.

The Nature of Standard Work

There is a true nature about Standard Work that I have come to really appreciate and I think the common shop floor employee does too. I will typically use or direct attention to these "points of nature" to help convince (never coerce) process operators that they will be better off with Standard Work. For some, this short list might come off as a little bit too Zen for a manufacturing book, but take a step back and consider for a second that there can be a nature to something like Standard Work and if we understand it, it will make even more sense.

Honesty: Standard Work is nothing if not honest, especially as it comes from the first hand witnessing of the process in action. The Time Observation is just such an honest approach to getting to know what is **truly** going on. Other approaches to gathering information in order to "standardize work" include interviewing the operator. Imagine, though, that the operator is unclear on whether he is supposed to tell you how the process "is supposed to work", or if he is supposed to tell you every small variation that has ever happened within the process. On the other hand, things that over the years he has consistently compensated for, that he simply does not recognize them as such. There is baked in a huge assumption that the operator even knows if the process is "supposed to work" or if he is just meant to have to adapt and overcome. Is the operator correct? Did he leave anything out? Why even discuss that? If all you want to know is what will happen during the course of the very next process cycle and maybe a few more, than watch and see. The process will tell you and nobody was lying. There was no influence from left or right as to what would be put down in writing. To the observer, the process just is. And finally, *you can't unsee stuff*. Once observed, if there are problems, if safety is compromised, if the process can't be performed twice the same way, the observer can't unsee it. It becomes an honest matter of record, and hopefully, discussion. Documenting reality!

Objectivity: The old "What is Value vs. what is Non Value" argument seems to be a never-ending one with perspectives often being driven by what always had to be done to make the process happen. In my plant(s), this sometimes had nothing to do with adding value, but may be about transacting the part in the system or where the finished part gets located. Trying to "explain" why certain things are being done is far less effective than armed with remedial knowledge of the eight classical wastes, observe and see how much / how often those wastes are part of the process at hand. No judgment. No justification why, just that they were present in the process. Standard Work is as objective as "it is what it is". If you can be objective about whether those things that "are" in the process are value added or waste and then act accordingly, but as to whether or not they are happening; objective observation.

Clarity: The simple tools of Standard Work and Time Observation are just that, simple – non complicated. And they make clear the relationship between the man and the machine. It makes quite clear, the intended order of tasks to be performed for success. There is no mistake about whether the operator expects to step around the work cell or if he bounces like a pinball, (we would hope not). It becomes clearly stated when automated cycles start and when they come to an end; if the operator has to wait for the machine or if it is the other way around. Moreover, what becomes most clear is whether the process is still working just the same or if things have changed. This can normally be determined, Standard Work in hand, by watching one cycle.

Power: Add all these attributes together and they tend to create a power around that discussion about that particular process. I have spent time in corrective action meetings in response to non-conforming parts and discussed everything from operator accountability (by way of punitive measures), to whether we really know when the part was actually made, to if we think the parts would work as is. All these approaches neglect the idea that we really know what is happening through the process in the first place. In this case, I mean, "really know" as opposed to perceive what the process should be doing when we find out that things actually work quite different than the perceptions are. Just walking up to the process and observing especially when looking at it through previously written Standard Work, answers all the above issues in one stop shopping; that stop, of course, must be made on the shop floor where the work is being done. Any other approach simply lacks the certainty of current reality to be as effective nearly as quickly. By that same token, many times I have picked up a Standard Work Combination Sheet and followed along with the operator to find that the process is operating just the same and that elements are even being performed within seconds of each time as stated in the elements of Standard Work that had been written two years prior. That tells me that if the elements of new Standard Work are followed a numbers of times without variation, that will translate into a physical execution that will itself not vary, even over time. I don't know a way more powerful to establish a process than write the Standard Work and discuss it with the operator or better yet, co-create with the operator.

Bob: ***"I have a bit of a rub here. Shingo and Ohno said that SW should change, at a minimum, every six months, in the spirit of CI."***

So there it is. Standard Work really does have a nature about it. As such, that nature observed and tapped into, Standard Work becomes **very organic**. It grows and develops with nurturing and attention. It withers and goes to sleep when ignored (good Standard Work, once written, never really dies unless the process goes away). *Standard Work is constantly trying to get your attention and tell you things.* It becomes a very good guide when we don't know what to do about a problem. It becomes a great comfort when trying to satisfy the customer. By all means, if you have started writing Standard Work in your organization you should start to feel these leanings. If you are not, then Standard Work's true nature has simply not internalized in you yet.

Bob: ***"Another way to look at SW is like a time bound road map. You want to drive from NYC to LA. You map it out. You add time. That sets an expectation. Did you get to LA on time? If not, the time bound map (your SWCS will TELL YOU***

WHAT WENT WRONG AND WHEN). A SWCS sets an expectation, AND is the diagnostic tool, ALL IN ONE!"

The Duality of Standard Work

Bob Pentland used to use a very simple model to try to communicate with us what really describes a **duality of journey paths** that will be taking place if an organization properly uses Standard Work in their LEAN transitions; one on the surface and the other one residing in the fabric of the company's socio cultural fabric. Bob draws a simple 2-axis matrix like the one below (see figure 4-1):

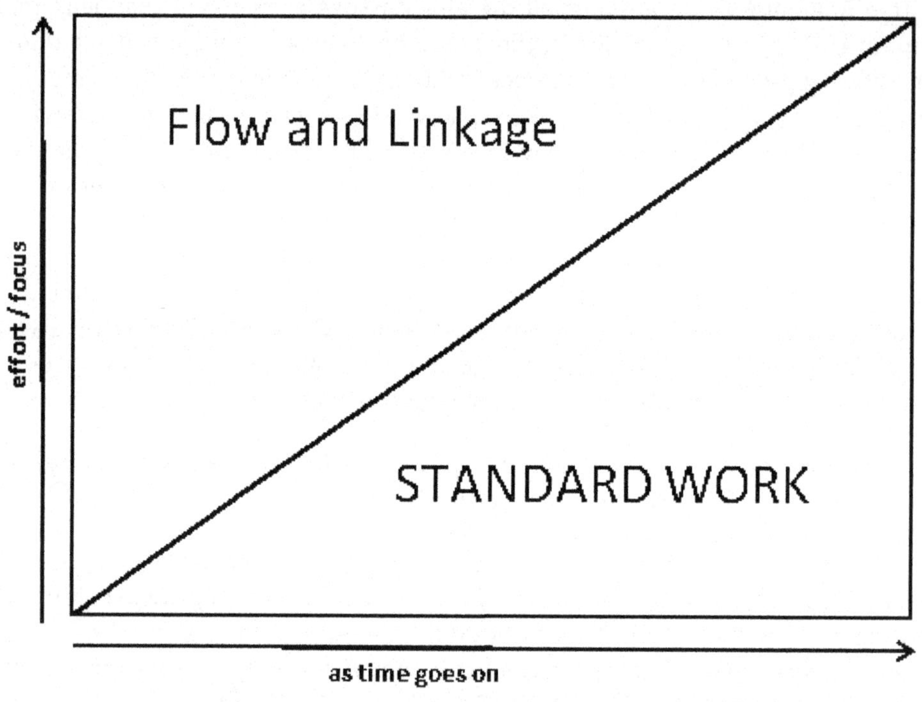

Figure 4-1: Flow and Linkage / Standard Work Matrix

The horizontal axis represents the passing of time and the vertical one is a picture of the sum of the resources available to work on the LEAN transition and how and where they spend that time (F&L or SW). If you read this chart from left to right, you will see that it shows how most companies start their journey; doing a lot of work on Kaizen type events like creating "Flow and Linkage" (that one is always exciting); doing SMED events (that one is really important); promoting 5S around the shop; and starting to set up and practice other Future State Behaviors. In the beginning, Standard Work seems like a follow up activity. After the new process is in place, we come back and write the Standard Work for it and VIOLA! When you say it like that, the graph and those proportions of Kaizen effort to Standard Work effort depicted way towards the left side of the graph are about correct to reality. And we leave Standard Work in place as we go through the organization transforming, however, once Standard Work is written, Standard Work lives. What about all that organic stuff I was talking about earlier? The Standard Work you leave in place of the new processes is going to be speaking to you **every TT (or CT)**. You are not done with the area! *You have just begun. The Standard Work is going to want you to fix problems and get better.* AND the Standard Work will want you to rewrite it every chance necessary! “As time goes on” (the horizontal axis on the matrix) that Standard Work should be calling to you (if not the operators who are wondering when you are going to return). *The kind of work we are doing with the Standard Work shifts from performing Time Observations and Writing Standard Work to using it to generate opportunities to fix the process and RE-write Standard Work* (or re-commit to supporting the cycle expectation; wherever you are in life with that process). It would stand to reason that more contact with Standard Work as maintaining LEAN processes continues would overtake the time spent on the Kaizen type activities that described what was happening in the early days. The model inverts (as you read it to the right) until finally, we are about through the transformation and into the internalized working of the LEAN Operating System, which features (Ta Da) Standard Work! **We live by it. We work to it. We consult it during times of trouble. We use it to train process operators. We use it to drive visual controls**. Standard Work - Standard Work - Standard Work. I think I have been clear. Standard Work is a verb. While “Flow and Linkage” generate “one time benefits, **Standard Work is “the gift that keeps on giving** for as we pursue SW, and remove waste, it provides the opportunity to revisit the F&L and tighten it up, or extend it further upstream and downstream.

What about this duality business? Let’s take what we just discussed and apply it to the deeper component, which describes a point in the journey from a more internal perspective. In the beginning of a LEAN journey, there is much to learn and practice. It is not always apparent why we are doing what we are doing but we have discussed that practice creates belief, so we do those things. As more and more waste is made visible, the action is to go do Kaizen type activities. There is usually a team that is assembled for many of these activities for both the sake of engaging employees and training them as well in the tools and ways of LEAN. There is much to DO in the opening throws of a LEAN initiative, AND DO-ing is the only way. There is stuff to DO that takes most people out of their comfort zone as well as out of their conventional work descriptions (at first and forever until the convention changes). There will be wonderful gains to be made which will inspire the organization to DO more LEAN things. So what is an organization going for in this regard – ultimately? If you think about it in the same context as the simple **Flow and Linkage / STANDARD WORK** matrix, if an organization endeavors to DO LEAN things and follows the path, it stands to reason that that organization should ultimately want to BE a LEAN organization; by specific description; by outward recognition; by internalized existence; BE LEAN. *I no longer "have" to do it; I "want" to do it.*

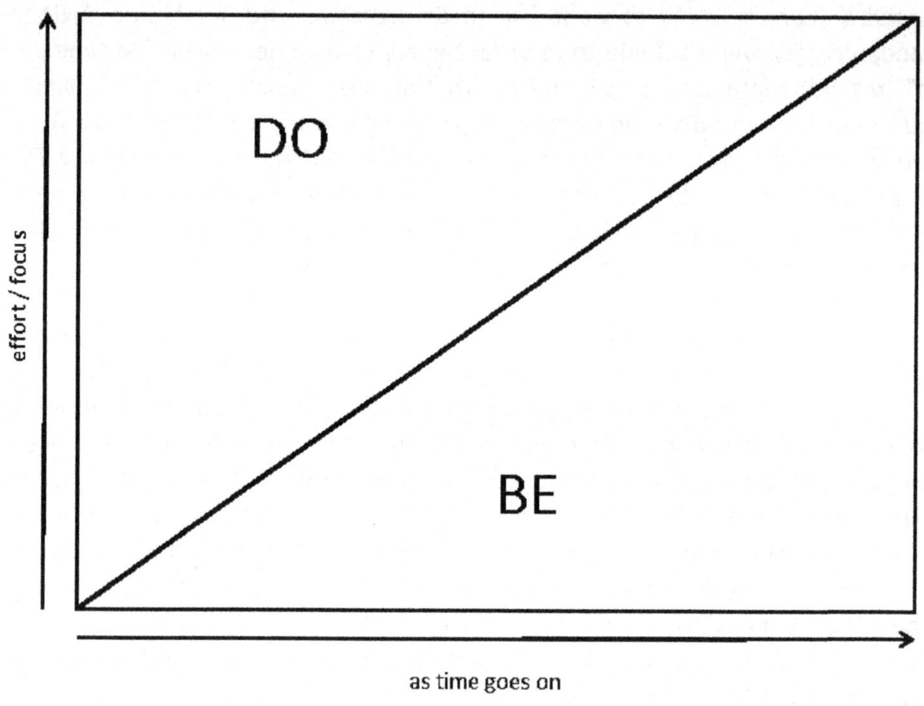

Figure 4-2: Do / Be Matrix

That having been said, the same **Flow and Linkage / STANDARD WORK** matrix becomes the **DO / BE** matrix (see figure 4-2), the initial connection being that Kaizen type activities are the vehicle for initial LEAN thinking going on out there. After all, we can go to classrooms up the butt or read every book, but eventually, we have to go out and do some things- make some changes- BE WILLING TO MAKE SOME CHANGES (not as easy as it was for me to type just now). The key to doing lies in all the action activities and tools that come in the LEAN package and that includes that we have to go DO (establish, create, write) Standard Work. It is the time to connect with the WANTS of the company to pursue DO-ing the right thing once and for all AND create and sustain Future State Behaviors to support that WANT.

The truly substantial connection between the two matrices is that "as time goes on" Standard Work becomes the BE in the journey. What Bob is trying to say here is that staging Kaizen Events, Time Observations and even writing Standard Work is not the end and won't, by itself, get you there in terms of true process stability, truly bulletproof quality, Continuous Improvement that extends way beyond "low hanging fruit". There is so much more to do, and it begins with performing each Takt Time to the cycle of the Standard Work and comparing performance to the intended Least Waste Way and when a problem arises, we fix it and get better. All these activities are done around the glow of the Standard Work campfire. As work is being done, all questions are directed through the Standard Work of the process. When the work is done and verified, all changes are incorporated into the new Standard Work and then the cycle repeats itself. This cycle describes what it actually looks like to BE LEAN in your organization. We've actually gotten there in our discussion here in this book (if only at a "Higher Level of Standard Work Talk", anyway). If a company is truly to get to the point of BE-ing LEAN, it will be because they are working their Standard Work through their processes, patiently and without end because they "want" to.

The simple models presented here are precisely that, simple, and the mindset that drives these models is also simple. *No complicated math or reports, just the processes.* So why would any of this be so hard for most companies to switch to? It is because of how far the basic business mind is from accepting anything that is as simple as this concept of creating a delivery system creating value in the shortest possible time with the highest possible quality for the lowest possible cost by way of featuring the process through Standard Work. There is conflict with the conventions of cost accounting and there is conflict with some of the mantras of top down management structures. There are sacred cows all over; MRP, economic order quantity to name a few, that folks will jealously defend. Finally, there is the misperception that nobody has time to do all that Standard Work stuff. We are all too busy trying to run the company that we don't have time to run the company. These aren't easy demons to exorcise. Thank goodness that the learning matrices are simple in structure. We create the realities in our companies that lead to overproduction, over processing, scrap, and other wastes hiding in plain sight under the protection of our own bureaucracy. It has been such a long strange trip just to get to dysfunction, who has the time to change it? I am saying we do! The time is there and the new types of activities that will help us are themselves simple in nature. Clear some space and work with them. In the end, you will wind up making more time than you are spending.

Bob: *"Crazy (affectionate term) George Koenigsaecker was known to say of the Toyota Production System, "It is either that easy (simple), or that complex." Simple does not appeal to the high and mighty."*

There is one more point of Duality that must be brought up. The LEAN journey through Flow and Linkage and on into Standard Work (or Doing to Being) will provide a productivity reward. Almost from the first moments of simply listening to your process (and operators), basic output will increase. Just start fixing things and where do you think that curve is heading. Great! Right?

Bob has a specific warning along these very lines:

"The theme of 'where will the resources come from' at a point REVERSES. That is, I would tell potential clients, "The tools of the TPS work. We are not going to discuss them. The only question is whether you can create the environment for them to flourish. AND, used aggressively you will generate as much as 25% productivity per year. We are NOT going to lay off people, so, you need to grow the business 25% year over year to absorb the excess people."

Now this **is** a fly in the ointment. But how fast can you say "over before it started" when the workforce reductions that correlate to a LEAN rollout come down. I have seen personally; owners who promised that there would be no layoffs as a direct result to the LEAN initiative, only to hear them praise the cost reducing efforts on the shop floor and then use economic downturn to facilitate "right sizing the workforce" for the current business case. To say it aloud almost makes it sound reasonable (I mean, who can control an economic downturn? Right?), but the damage to the company's credibility, to the company's resolve could easily mitigate the savings. It could also bring the journey to an unceremonious halt. It is often discussed that change during slow periods is ideal, and in some ways that makes sense, but what if you are busily putting people to work doing exciting things and the accountant is whispering in the CEO's ear saying, "We have 6 people too many."

CHAPTER 5 – Cycle Time = Takt Time

Waste Hides in the Cracks

Waste: defects; inventory; over production; over processing; waiting; excess motion; transportation; AND wasting the time of your most precious resource - people. Waste is pervasive. Even in the best-intended environments, if you leave your back turned for just a moment, the gremlins of waste attach themselves to your process without even your noticing – at first. And waste is not always obvious about where or how it creeps in. Waste likes pauses or breaks in the activity as well as the normal routine tasks. Waste likes for you to start and stop often. Waste likes to romance folks into rationalizing the creation of "piles" in order to amortize more waste. It is for this very reason that creating flow is so important. It is because the elimination of repetitive starting and stopping in essence squeezes waste out of those cracks. Think of the waste that is involved in the end of an operation or the start of another. There is putting the traveling paperwork together with the 'pile' and then someone has to move the 'pile' to the location of the next operation. There will probably be labor reporting, a long laborious set up, and, of course, all the forklift traffic. How much waste could find its way into THAT collection of activities? How many of those activities are in fact, waste as well in and of themselves? And so, we create single piece flow to eliminate those cracks that waste can hide in. And, one-piece flow puts a premium on Real Time Problem Resolution. By that same logic, it is equally important to fully "load" the folks working in process areas; that is to say, give them enough value adding work to fill the time they have available for working on that process. It may seem like keeping a buffer of time to help make shipping demands "protects" the process. That is actually not the case at all. In fact, the opposite is true. If you have a few good folks who only really have half or three quarters of a workload wandering in and out of their respective processes, then waste will surely come in and DESTROY your good processes and before you know it, you NEED that extra time you've baked in just to get things done (and often times poorly at that). Motivated employees will tend to use excess time to compensate for things that go wrong (waste that creeps in) thus covering up opportunities for improvement. For this reason, before any real sustainable Continuous Improvement can take place, the time available planned for the resources and the percent load of work to occupy them (the cycle times) have to be made as close to equal as possible. Doing so will serve to expose waste by squeezing on waste's favorite hiding places. I love to squeeze waste there. It is almost a given that some immediate benefit pops out, even without being real creative at first pass. Just getting real with your customer requirement provides benefit. Everyone would claim to be paying attention to that, of course, but the difference here is that by creating a cognitive linkage between the resource plan and the target output and trying to match that resource to the need, a discreet expectation of customer support can be created and maintained as its own visual control- WITH EVERY INTENTION OF LEAVING NOTHING FOR THE WASTE! Cycle Time = Takt Time is page one of the two page book that my friend, Bob, threatens to write (I bet we've written way more than two pages together here for sure!). He taught us that it was our responsibility to the customer and to the stakeholders to demonstrate how we were going to satisfy customer demand with a document that made it clear that specific consideration of the customer's demand is and the resource dedicated to satisfying it. Capacity reports routinely overstate capacity in terms of available machine time.

Bob says, *"I have also seen many situations whereby the potential capacity is totally diluted by taking into account equipment downtime or scrap, repair, supplier issues as facts of life (as an aside, when I bought a $60M engine block line at Chrysler, we discounted the designed capability of the machine by 50%)."*

We already redefined "cycle time" NOT as just machine cycle time but TOTAL PROCESS TIME including post processing tasks performed by the HUMANS (SWCS – combination of "man and machine") in the organization, SOooo getting right with the process Standard Work and then having a way of showing that Standard Work's reason for existing (through the percent load to support a customer) is the better way and it is a vital set up for Continuous Improvement. To Bob, it is fully half of the LEAN end game.

Takt Time Talk

Takt Time (the beat, the rhythm, of the customer) is not necessarily misunderstood, but rather often spoken out of context to the process that we are trying to calculate the Percent Load for. "Time Available divided by Sold Units", the calculation for Takt Time, is not in itself hard to understand. But, in order for Takt Time (the "tool"), to be useful in the Percent Load calculation of a resource, the "sold units" part of the quotient must relate specifically to what the resource provides for the customer. For instance, if we sold 1000 pumps but only half of them get "the bushing" in them, then the bushing cell's Takt Time denominator is 500, not 1000. If the "bushing cell" makes bushings for more than one product line, then maybe the bushing cell's Takt Time denominator is the original 500 + another 650 for another pump model + 300 from another for a total Takt Time denominator of 1450 (pieces).

Finally, the Time Available / Sold Units calculation must be done using a consistent interval for both the numerator and the denominator: Time Available over "a day" / sold units over "a day". If the conversation moves to a new perspective- "a year" or "a shift", the units of time for both the top and bottom of the Takt Time quotient must agree or else mathematical relativity is lost. It is important to be able to visualize Takt Time with respect to the process at hand. If it is a continuous process delivering a discreet product to a customer, an enterprise level Takt Time may be appropriate but if you live in a mixed model environment where products and customers share resources, that resource's portion of the Time Available and the Customer Demand will have to be broken out in order to use Takt Time as the LEAN tool that it really is. Takt Time is a VERB!

"REAL" Time Available

Time, as mentioned before, is precious and irreplaceable. It is also objective and you can't *game* time. We must take care not to be flip about casting away time available, by any means. But realistically, process operators don't have WHOLE 8 hours to run their processes. There are break times and times for the operator to wash up (some of these are even compelled by employment law). There is legitimate preventative maintenance that can only be done when the machine is not running, there is 5S (Sort-Straighten-Shine-Standardize-Sustain) and there is material management (in a pull environment). How does each of these tasks affect the time available to make parts or run the process? There is only one way to find out. Lay it out realistically hour-by-hour and calculate what your organization actually supports in the way of time available. Here is a simple example: If an hour equals 3600 seconds (and we always do this in seconds), then 3600 * 8 = 28,800 seconds of time available per 8 hour shift (excluding a non-paid lunch). Without paying overtime, that's all there is: 28,800". Next, our organization has a mandated 900" break (15 minutes) in both the morning and the afternoon. There is also the expectation that the operator gets to leave their area 300" (5 minutes) early to wash his hands before lunch and 600" (10 minutes) to sweep up at the end of his shift ***("And we should have a SWCS for this as well."* B.P.)**. So that comes to:

28,800
-1,800 (2 breaks)
-900 (wash and sweep)
=26,100 total time available per shift.
(Your organizations will vary)

If there are other elements that take away from time available, then they need to be noted and dealt with (for example, operator PM at the start of the shift). Bear in mind that you don't want to indiscriminately remove time available. If the task is deemed important enough to sacrifice time available, then the Standard Work for doing it gets written; then and only then should you calculate it out.

Bob Coaches, *"Every deduction from the TA will make you less competitive. If you are operating two shifts then it is double as you will be dividing by the ADD (average daily demand). Again, no factor is included for equipment down time as 'the equipment is to run when we want it to run'. Likewise, there is no allowance for raw material not present, or, if present and not unusable."*

Percent Load and the Takt Time Line

The focus on the percent load is to show the relationship between either the Takt Time with a single process cycle time OR the Time Available with the average run time expectation over the same period (like daily). Another way to think of this is some number of Takt Times (depicted as the line) and the SAME number of cycle times (depicted as the bar). Properly calculated, both the 'Takt Time to Cycle Time' and the 'Time Available to Average Daily Run Time' ratios turn out the same.

In a mixed model environment the ADRT (average daily run time which is the WACT times the Average Daily Demand) must be equal to the Time Available. This is the mixed model surrogate for CT=**TT ("I always like to show the TT in red on all my documents as it IS the customer" B.P.)** and I will further develop the mixed model scenario a bit later. The Percent Load can be drawn on the Standard Work Sheet that was introduced earlier in the LEAN tools chapter

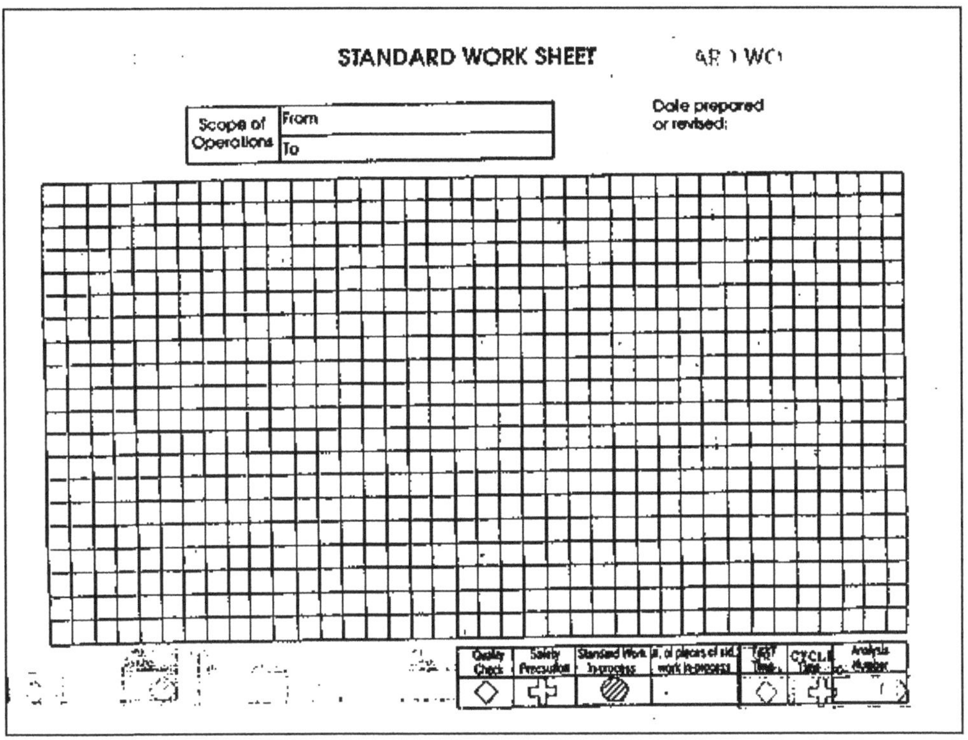
STANDARD WORK SHEET

Scope of Operations	From
	To

Date prepared or revised:

Quality Check	Safety Precaution	Standard Work In-process	# of pieces of std. work in-process	Takt Time	Cycle Time	Analysis Number

Figure 5-1: SWS to be used to draw Percent Load

I prefer to use the Standard Work Sheet to draw the Percent Load (see figure 5-1) mostly because it makes very good graph paper and there should always be one of these forms around, but Percent Load can really be drawn on any blank sheet a paper. Percent Load is typically expressed as a bar chart (hence the graph paper reference).

To show the relationship between the Takt Time (per part) and a Cycle Time (per part) start by drawing a line near the bottom and another line near the left side of the graphing window. Scale the vertical line so that the Takt Time (in seconds) would be drawn about three quarters up the sheet on the scale. Draw the Takt Time line across in red at that point. Now you can take your Standard Work cycle time and make a bar just to the right of the vertical line, sized appropriately to the time scale of the vertical line. Below is an example of a single operator running a cycle compared to a Takt Time calculation.

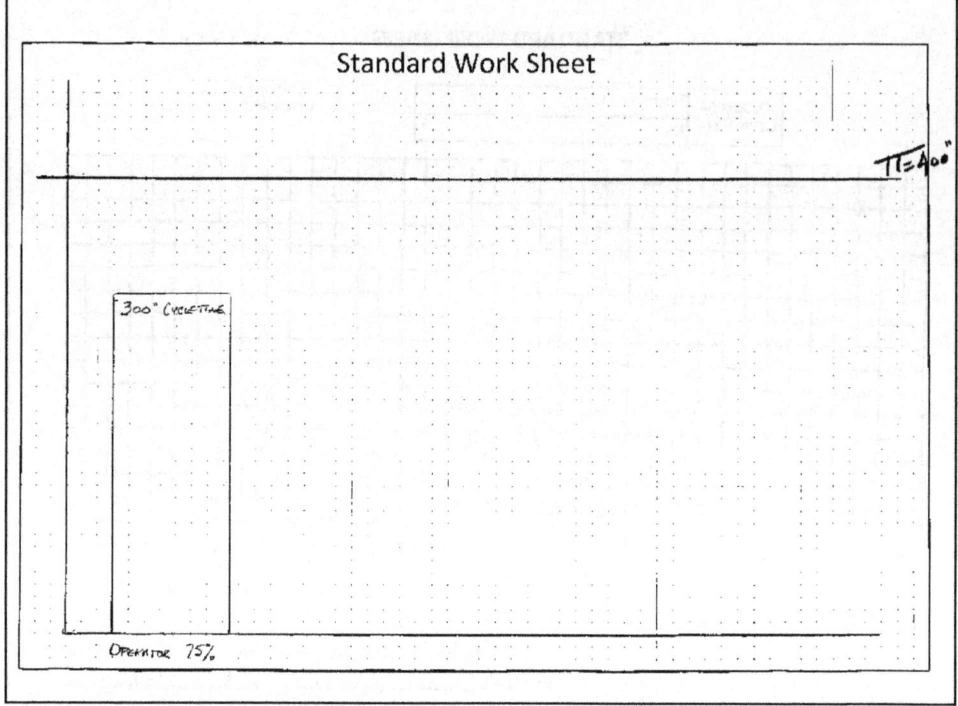

Figure 5-2: Percent Load Example 1

In the case depicted above (see figure 5-2), this operator's cycle time is about 75% of the Takt Time. The opportunity is to pull value added elements into that operator's cycle so that it better matches the Takt Time (and those elements must be of the same TT). This can be done by looking upstream and downstream in the flow (again, assuming the same TT). It takes the Takt Time calculation and the expression of Percent Load to SEE this opportunity. The operator is not likely to sit by idly, cycle by cycle and let 25% of his time pass by. He will instead make parts as fast as he can and maybe create a pile of them (inventory is a waste). And, as waste comes in to attack him, he will use that 25% time buffer to overcome the waste rather than eliminate it- all because we could not see the delta between his REAL cycle time and the Customer's "cycle time": Takt Time. In the case of this operator, it would be much more important that this operator come closer to finishing (or starting) the product than it would be for him to make more of the semi complete items (assuming there is more to do downstream- or upstream in the same flow).

Processes that have multiple operators working to the same process, can have multiple operators bars on the same percent load chart expressed under that same Takt Time line, but only if they are working to the same Takt Time, in reality. For the sake of clarity, I am referring to a continuous process of multiple operators: same customer (or customer profile); same customer demand (or distribution); same time available.

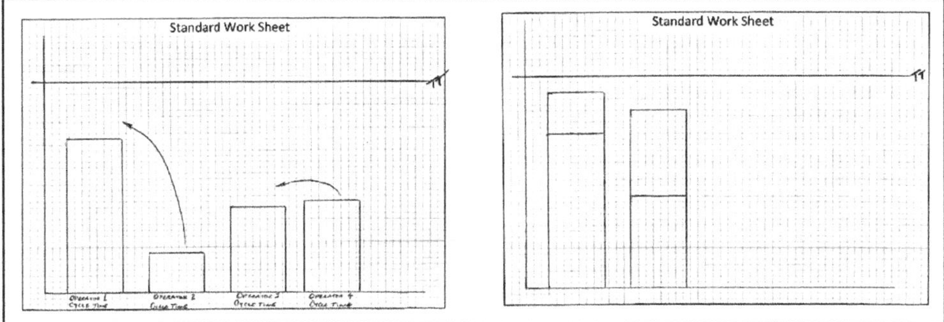

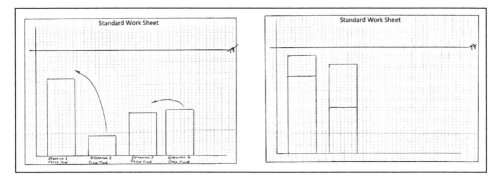

Figure 5-3: Percent Load Example 2

They could all be drawn in bars next to each other to the right of the vertical line (see figure 5-3). In the example above on the left, you can see that the overall process is segmented into four different cycles each performed by a different operator. The opportunity that is depicted on the right is to combine the individual cycles and in doing so, there is work to fill out only two operators, and still with room to spare (for nasty/ugly/wasteful things to happen, by the way. Notice that the space between the Takt Time line and the top of the now (2) bars is much smaller, though. By combining the four separate operations into two (by creating flow and linkage), the remaining newly combined cycle times are much closer to the Takt Time. Doing this in essence squeezes the space that waste could hide in. Combining elements into cycles that equal the Takt Time is something completely different from "level loading" in the industrial engineering sense. Level loading opens us up to the risk of overproduction and in fact perpetuates the over cost of the current operation.

"Given the element size, the layout, and other factors, we would want to load the first operator 100%. It also makes it more evident as to the opportunity to redeploy an operator by highlighting the minimal amount of waste required to do so. The Shingijutsu manual has a good visual (see figure 5-4 – a page from the original manual from 1987)." **Bob.**

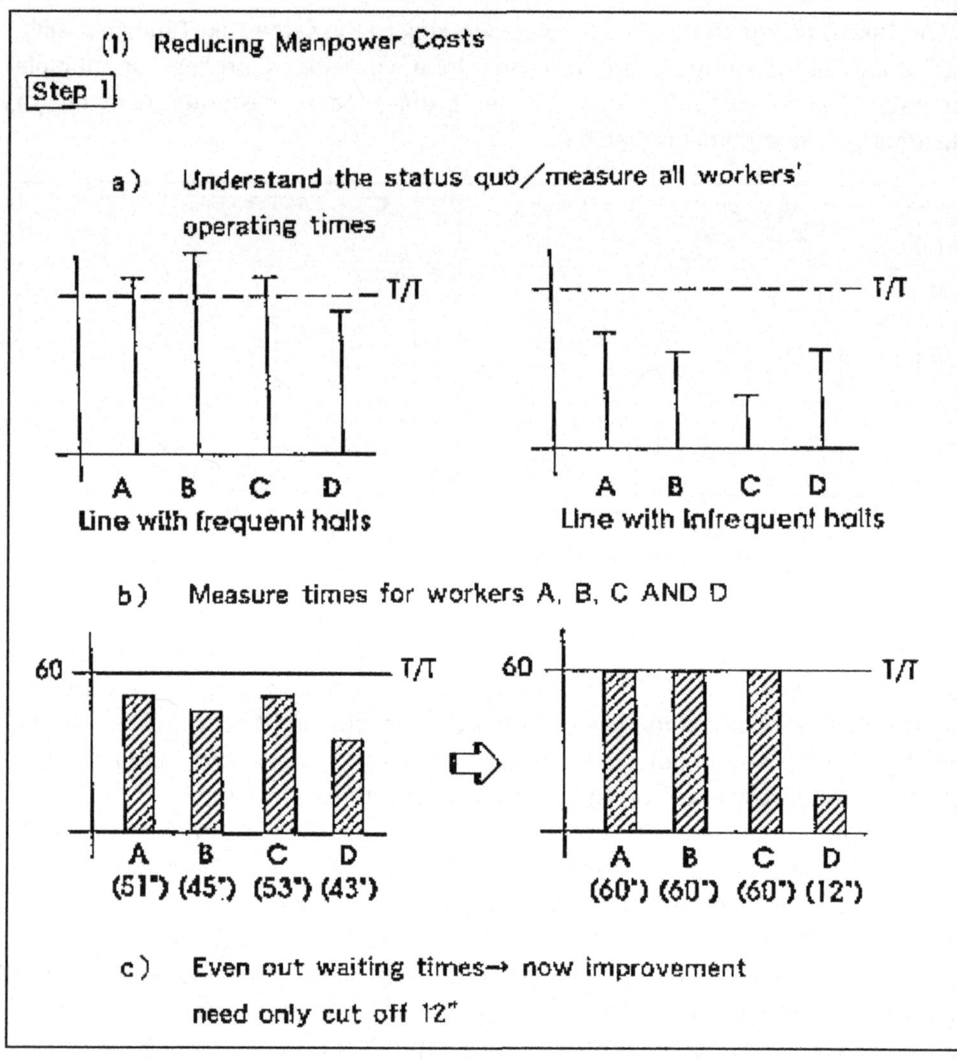

Figure 5-4: Page from the Original Playbook

There is one other way to make Cycle Time equal to Takt Time and that would be to REDUCE the Time Available to match the output and then redeploy the people. This approach is problematic in that it dismisses opportunities to become better at our processes. Rather than making Cycle Time = Takt Time by eliminating waste, reducing Time Available simply forces the equation. The main point in my mentioning this perspective is to say if we commit too much resource to a process, we bake cost into the process, whether we like it or not. A much better way of thinking of the delta between a fixed cycle time and the Takt Time would be that the delta represents capacity that must be filled.

Bob warns, "For me there has always been an issue of reducing the TA. What do I do with the operator? Managing this on the shop floor, for me, is VERY difficult. I always warned potential clients that they would need to increase sales. The above gaps could also be closed by increasing sales."

Percent Load and the Time Available Line (mixed model environment)

Percent load can be written using the relationship between Average Daily Run Time to Time Available just the same as for the relationship between Cycle Time to Takt Time. The two ratios are related and if the calculations are done correctly, the percentage of each will be equivalent. This point is easily proven with the calculation on the right side of the document shown below (see figure 5-5).

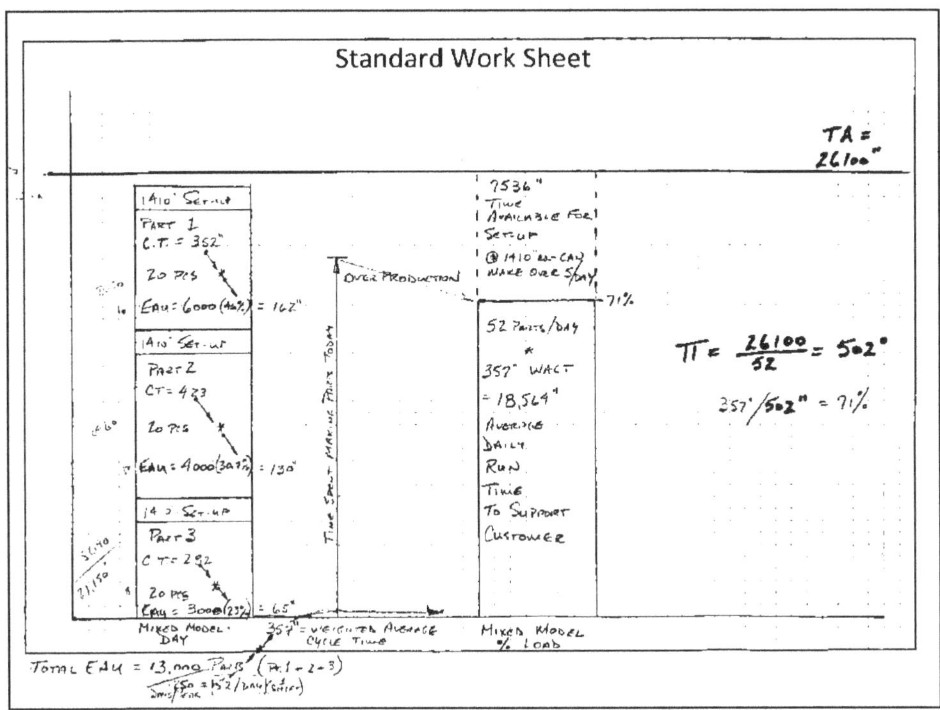

Figure 5-5: Percent Load Example 3

Establishing an Expectation

The left bar in the example above shows a "day in the life" scenario in which three different parts that share the same assets (operator - work cell) were set up and run; 20 pieces each (perceived economic order quantities driven by forecast).

The red line depicts the Daily Time Available of resources dedicated to make that family of parts. Each of the three part numbers have different cycle times and different EAUs. By multiplying the cycle times by the part number's relative percentage of the total, we can create a "Weighted Average Cycle Time" for the part family. Then by multiplying the WACT by the average parts per day to satisfy the customer across all parts, we can calculate the Average Daily Run Time, which is the bar depicted on the right. You may notice that the vertical line between the two bars (the actual time that was used to make parts on the day of the left bar) is a bit higher, indicating 2586" more time spent making parts. If a cell were to do this every day, the company would be in jeopardy of over producing. The additional time is being filled by making parts. What other activities could that time be better used doing and why concern ourselves with percent load anyway?

Preventing Overproduction

In the example above (left side), it may have seemed to the company that running 20 parts for each setup was the best thing to do, but through the Percent Load, it can be seen that there is over production occurring and the opportunity to set up some of the part numbers "more often" exists which could have the effect of lowering inventory levels and being more responsive to the customer-especially if his needs change from time to time. Another opportunity revealed by this Percent Load is to look upstream and down to see if there was more processing that could be added to the single piece flow. Increasing the cycle time will not impact customer satisfaction if still not exceeding the Time Available. Alternatively, since setup might be a current fact of life in the mixed model type environment, being able to calculate how many setups can be done per year can be used to set the run quantities. In a mixed model environment, you have to run each part number at least once per year, but that doesn't mean you can't run them 10, 20, 50 times per year if you have the setup time to do it.

Bob says, *"PLEASE REMEMBER THE TOYOTA DEFINITION OF SET UP, 'FROM LAST GOOD PIECE TO NEXT GOOD PIECE'. WE ALWAYS WANT TO CAPTURE 'ADJUSTMENT' OR 'GETTING QUALITY'. AS SUCH, EVERY SET UP WILL MANUFACTURE ONE PART OR ASSEMBLY FOR THE CUSTOMER! IT GETS A LITTLE STICKY HERE IN THE MIXED MODEL ENVIRONMENT WHEN WE DO NOT HAVE ENOUGH TIME BETWEEN THE AVERAGE DAILY RUN TIME AND THE TIME AVAILABLE TO DO ENOUGH SET UP TO SUPPORT 'ONE OF EVERYTHING THE CUSTOMER WANTS EVERY DAY'. THIS LEADS INTO A DISCUSSION OF KANBAN/MRS. (By the way, Kanban's are a halfway house. By successive SMED's, thus reducing the set up time, the goal is to attain one piece flow)."*

Supporting the "EQUATION" = Customer Satisfaction

Making Cycle Time Equal to Takt Time describes the equation that is intended to link satisfying the customer to the resources to be used by filling the Time Available with Standard Work tasks while creating the equation that drives Continuous Improvement. If the customer intel is good and you have written your Standard Work, then by simply supporting the equation of the Percent Load, you can be assured of supporting the customer and success can be measured cycle time by cycle time; Takt Time by Takt Time.

By committing the customer requirement to a percent load, we can take an estimated annual usage and boil it down to a daily requirement that will satisfy the customer, and if maintained, will satisfy him the whole year- unless something changes and, in turn, you are squeezing out waste by leaving no time behind for it to attack. In fact, the whole function of the Percent Load lends it to becoming the Standard Work for its own Continuous Improvement cycle. Whenever we get results "other" than the expectation at the level that describes a Percent Load, then there becomes an opportunity to understand the difference and fix or recalibrate – IN TIME NOT TO DISSATISFY THE CUSTOMER. Good news, right?

CHAPTER 6 - The Continuous Improvement Cycle

Philosophical Perspective: Continuous Improvement

The term, "Continuous Improvement" just rolls off the tongue like butter off a hot biscuit, but I doubt that most organizations actually have a visual concept of what Continuous Improvement looks like (or will look like) in their enterprise. It's not their fault for misunderstanding. The term, "continuous improvement" has been used as a "catch all," "buzz word" term and is at risk of overuse. We have continuous improvement engineers, continuous improvement boards, continuous improvement quality circles and some organizations have actually acronym-ized it, "CI," just to be able to save time saying it. See! Continuous Improvement already! But what are we really going for? What are we trying to continuously improve on and why? And most importantly, when we get better at doing something, how do we insure that the improvement is translated to the bottom line and that it's not just given back to the waste in a short time.

It is helpful to get clear on the notion of Continuous Improvement and compare it to a more common approach: breakthrough level improvement. When big changes in a process with the expectation of a drastic increase in output are made, that is the result of a "breakthrough improvement." Breakthrough improvements are dependent on technological advancements, sweeping design, or process change and can often times be very expensive (featuring cap ex investments in the latest technology or moving of monuments or the slaying of dragons). Continuous Improvement is focused on the incremental elimination of waste and on fixing those things that have gotten in the way of performing the Standard Work cycles perfectly. Continuous Improvement also focuses on re-establishing the new way (every improvement iteration) so the new process can be performed flawlessly and to combat the ultimate slide back (give back of the gain) if you don't. Without this last part, Continuous Improvement will just turn out to be re-improving over and over again and that's just rework; and that, in itself, is a waste.

Continuous Improvement needs a couple of things from those who wish to improve. For starters, it would be a good idea to ultimately understand what the organization is trying to achieve with respect to the customer. Without taking the customer's view, it is all too possible to target things for improvement that the customer doesn't actually assign value to. It just added cost that the customer won't be paying for. So, improve on things that the customer really wants, *in the eyes of the customer, and NOT yours.* They want it to have a higher degree of precision: improve process capability. They want more and more parts: improve throughput velocity. They want all the colors and they want which ones they want now: improve change over. Oh by the way, *you* want to make more money: improve the cost to manufacture by eliminating waste.

Continuous Improvement also wants you to understand your process. There can be no assumptions baked in to a plan to continuously improve a process area like what the cycle time actually is, or whether the operator can actually perform the work as "perceived" by those who work in offices. The process must be able to be performed in a stable, repetitive way. The basic process path must be performed (able to be performed) without variation by the operator. We have already discussed the premier tool for finding this out about processes: documenting reality through Time Observation! Simply standing out by the process with your hands in your pockets to see if the operator is performing in a stable, cycle after cycle way will tell if the process is even ready for Continuous Improvement. Maybe you have to construct a legitimate process first.

Once established, Continuous Improvement is going to want a document to stand as the "Least Waste Way" of doing the process (that we currently know of) and I bet you know what I am going to write, don't you. Standard Work to the rescue! If you write the Standard Work, then you will have a campfire to talk about improvements around. You will be able to ask and answer questions of how something new might impact the current process cycle. All too often, countermeasures to problems are thrown at a process operator without any idea of how that new activity might impact the operator's ability to satisfy the customer; how they might impact the cycle time / percent load; whether focus from the existing elements Standard Work might be impaired. Standard Work (again).

Continuous Improvement is going to want you to practice your process and compare how it went to your expectation of the "least waste way"- with every cycle. *Why every cycle?* Simply put, every cycle is a chance to get better at the process and satisfy the customer. It is why Standard Work is written with the "return to start" element being so important. To run a continuously improving process, it needs to operate like a motor, where one cycle follows the last seamlessly. If there is time to stand around and collect thoughts or have a respite, then waste will come back into your process, hiding in the space between cycles.

Continuous Improvement is going to want cycles to run contiguously, without pause until it is time to turn off the engine altogether.

Finally, Continuous Improvement is going to want you to have a way to *SEE when the cycle could not be performed to the "least waste way" in real time when it happens!* This last one may seem like a tall order, but it is possible with a very simple visual control.

Plan Do Check Act (PDCA) – Hello Mr. Deming

I learned a couple of things in my reading up on Plan Do Check Act for the sake of historical accuracy and my sources (internet) are above reproach (LOL). I did not know that the PDCA that I have always errantly attributed to Deming was actually an adaptation of the scientific method model developed by Francis Bacon in the seventeenth century. In the early 1920s, a man named Walter Shewhart, while working at the Hawthorne plant of the Western Electric Company (ever hear of the Hawthorne Effect), adapted Bacon's model to depict how continuous improvement through statistical controls should work best. I believe that Deming met Mr. Shewhart and would refer to the "Shewhart Model" often in his discussions of PDCA. In any case, the model is not a new idea and has a place in any Continuous Improvement discussion. The model I am going to refer to in this section is the one you see below (see figure 6-1).

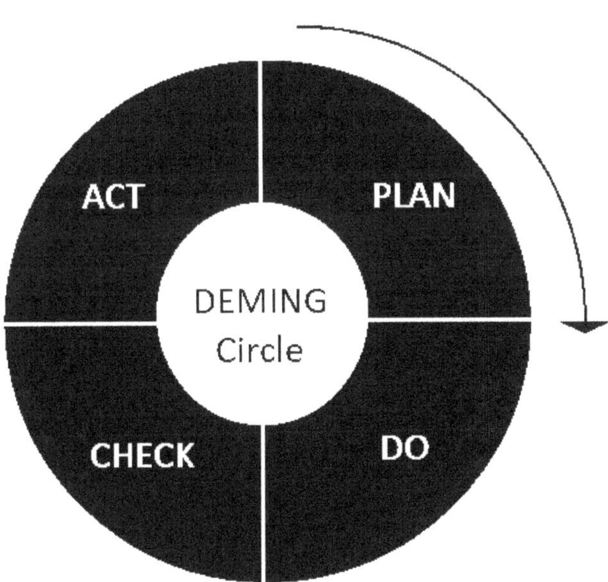

Figure 6-1: Deming's PDCA Cycle

The intention of the model with respect to Continuous Improvement is fairly simple:

Plan: ID what to improve and by what means
Do: Implement the change
Check: Measure the change outcomes
Act: Fix something if the outcome does not match the expectations

The Six Sigma boys also align with the PDCA model. Their improvement model acronym is DMAIC (Define, Measure, Analyze, Improve, Control; there are more words there, but I think improve and control belong together under Act). Whatever the origin, it is a universally recognized template for the Continuous Improvement cycle in the world. There is a major problem as far as I am concerned. It can still be difficult to tell if Continuous Improvement has taken place or what it looks like physically. At the end of the day, Shewhart's model was thought to be a rather smart piece of theory, but it lacked physical application and led to traction problems. So then, how does one instruct their problem solvers to go out to a process and conduct Continuous Improvement?

Activity Perspective: Basic Process Management

We have developed the discussion of Standard Work (a very **verby** word) and how it has very physical future state behaviors required to support it, and how Standard Work is the real physical extension of the more philosophical idea of standardized work (as it pertains to "Lean Thinking"). In this case, the Basic Process Management tool that I am going to introduce in this chapter is to Continuous Improvement as Standard Work is to "standardized work". It is the activity that supports the philosophy. The basic process management tool I am going to be discussing below is really just a collection of very simple but powerful tools (Standard Work: very simple but incredibly powerful, no?) working in concert to form the preeminent visual control on the LEAN shop floor. As a basic visual control model, it can be proliferated about the operation to stand and help manage processes, both manufacturing and administrative. The basic process management visual control will provide a focal point for Future State Behaviors to be executed and worked on, also serving as the file history of what has happened and what was done about it in each work cell. And finally, this visual control will, once and for all, provide visual objective evidence of Continuous Improvement *THAT CAN BE SEEN BY ANYONE, AND AT ANYTIME!* You will be able to take someone by the hand, show them the Continuous Improvement in the area, and explain what it looked like and what the process looks like now. Before we have everything we need to do all that, we need to pull a couple of thoughts together and line them up.

Working to Expectations

Let's further develop an illustration. As a process cycle is being run, and assuming we understand the Standard Work of the process, there is the expectation of results- the physical expectation of what came out of the process cycle. Was it correct quality wise? Did it come out of the process without struggle? Are we ready to do it again right away? Has something come along that requires attention before we can continue? Answers to these questions are constantly popping out of an established "least waste way" process with every cycle. In fact, that actually happens with every cycle of every process performed in our facilities. The main difference is that most of the time, opportunities pass without visibility of their occurrence of facility to capture the problems as they arise. Therefore, the fact is that the information required to continuously improve is and has always been there. The shortcoming is that our current methods of monitoring (productivity, effectivity metrics) do not see the occurrences that could lead to fixing systemic problems. So, what is needed is a way to use the "least waste way" to set an expectation of outcome so we can see if we don't hit it. The basis for EXPECTATION is TAKT TIME. At a level where a discreet process makes all the parts for a specific Takt Time ***"the beat, the rhythm of the customer"*** **(BP)**, the expectation of output is, in fact, literally equal to the customer Takt Time. In a mixed model environment, a weighted average cycle can be calculated to determine percent load, but as long as the Standard Work has been written and the customer requirement intel is pretty good, then we are back to performing to the Standard Work in play – and if we do, life is good.

So what is the punchline, here? The most effective tool there is to use to monitor the difference between the "least waste way" and the "last cycle performed" is TIME. Time is finite. It can't be made. **It can never be recovered**. It can only be spent and when we define how we plan to spend the time, we can figure out how to tell if the goal was met or not. If you can SEE if the cycle is running without issues, you can tell if the process is supporting the customer. Furthermore, we have to get real about resource availability, maintenance and PM attributed to the operator, all other things that amount to planned downtime.

Bob coaches, *"Unfortunately the word 'downtime', for some folks only means equipment downtime. We want to focus on stuff that 'takes away for the time available'. Any and all stuff."*

We simply don't make parts during planned downtime. If Takt Time has actually been calculated, then overall time available should already have been considered. But now it has to be taken to the shop floor. Exactly how much time during each hour of the shift are we going to make parts- by design? As tasks that delete from time available are considered, a deliberation over what and how much is a must. By that, I mean, no pat, general predictions of "uptime" (usually 80%), but instead, a critical list of tasks that are required of the operator to keep the machines and work area in good health to the advantage of "future uptime". AND, and, and, those tasks are represented by the specific Standard Work to perform those support tasks and the visual control to monitor (IF they are task that are REALLY worth sacrificing precious time available for). Here is a caveat for all you captains of industry who want to sharpen your pointing fingers; you can't wish some of these tasks away from existence by delegating to "others". In the real world of the process operator, those machines or that work area will need some amount of constant attention. Someone has to do that kind of work, too. Plan for it or it will make time.

The FRAM Oil Filter Commercial

"You can pay me now, or, you can pay me later."

There is a tool that I must introduce here and it facilitates the idea of working to Standard Work velocity expectations (is the cycle time equal to the Takt Time?). There is a danger associated with this tool in which it is used, as a productivity tool instead of a Continuous Improvement tool and the line between can be pretty fine- More on that in a bit. For now, let's look at a basic Hour-by-Hour Sheet (see figure 6-2).

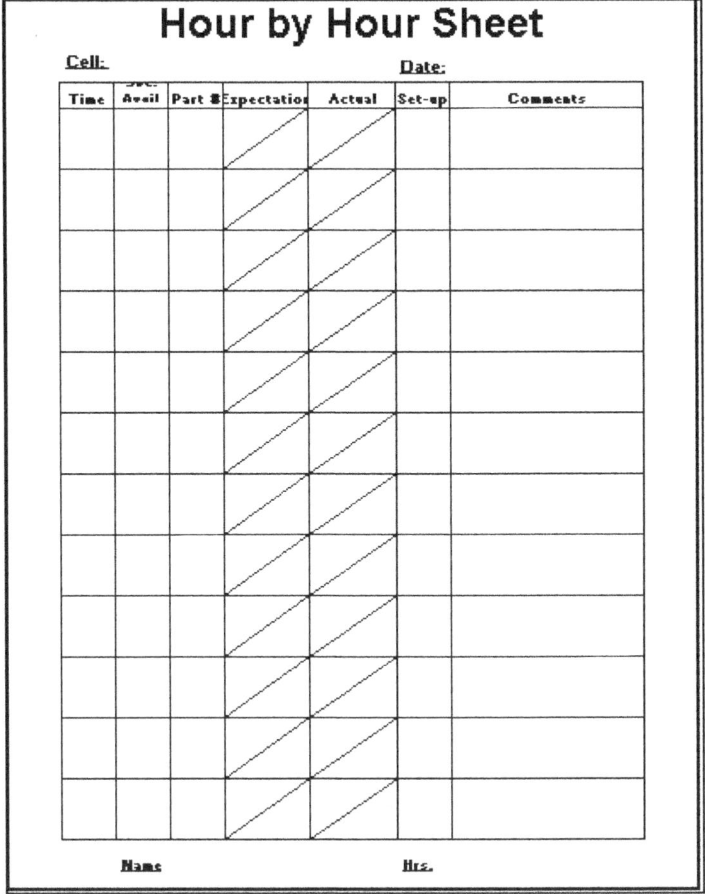

Hour by Hour Sheet

Cell: Date:

Time	Avail	Part #	Expectation	Actual	Set-up	Comments

Name Hrs.

Figure 6-2: Hour-by-Hour Sheet

Labor reporting is not itself a new concept. How it is viewed as a tool is where things get interesting. If we have straight in our operational mind when we have provided intended time available to run the process, then the expectation is simply the planned time available / the expected cycle time. Lay that across any given hour and an expectation of output has been established. The chart at hand is broken down to be able to work with hours of a day **IN REAL TIME**. That sure does beat the heck out of end of the day reporting where all that happened must be recalled, and thought processed so as to be able to fill out a labor ticket. The breakdown of a shift into eight increments means that the chance to set off an alarm in the case of not meeting expectations has been multiplied by 8.

This is only just a step, though, hence the self-limiting flaw of the Hour by Hour Chart. The true opportunity is to get to Takt Time by Takt Time. **Every time the**

process cycle is run is a chance to get better at doing it, and in reality, with the right work climate, the right culture, the operator will send up a flair at the first cycle where there is trouble! *"OTHERWISE, IN THE TOYOTA PRODUCTION SYSTEM, KNOWN AS 'LINE STOP'."* (B.P.) So, make no mistake here, folks, the Hour by Hour chart is meant to be a trainer to direct the mindset towards Takt Time by Takt Time. As a trainer, the Hour-by-Hour chart does serve a very important second function and that is as the visual physical representation of awareness to a running expectation of the process at hand, which is going to factor into Future State Behavior creating activity centered around the process visual control. No spoilers yet!

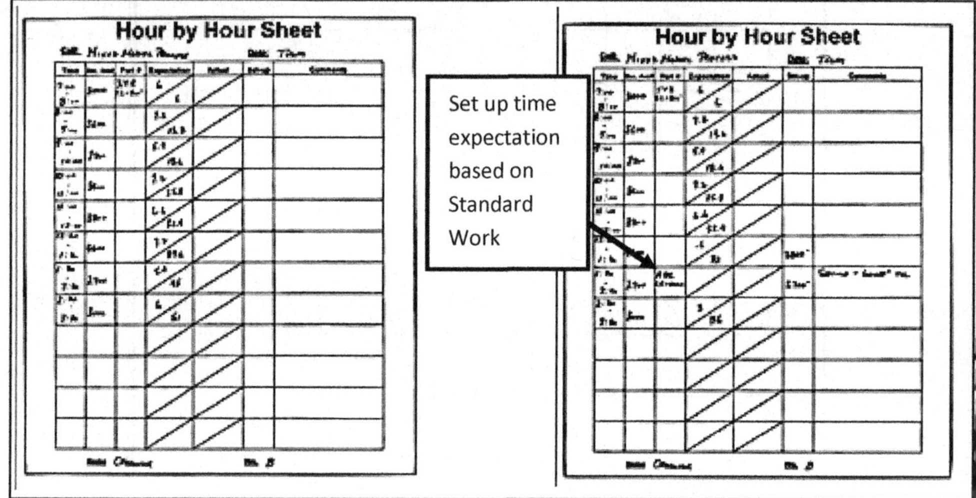

Figure 6-3: Hour-by-Hour Sheet Examples

Above (see figure 6-3) are depicted two sets of expectations laid out for the coming eight hours. The one on the right includes set up time and the run of a part with a different cycle time in a mixed model environment.

Ask WHY WHY WHY WHY WHY?

At some point, it is not enough just to SEE problems as they arise.

Bob: *"MY TEACHERS NEVER REFERRED TO THEM AS 'PROBLEMS'. THEY WERE TREASURES. THEY WERE PEARLS."*

We must DO something about those problems **(Opportunities)** as they arise. There is much to discuss on the subject of Real Time Problem Resolution, but it certainly starts with the idea of asking WHY when things go wrong at the moment of occurrence such that we a dealing with FACTS, not **"HYSTERICAL DATA."** It is really quite important to exercise the practice of stating the situation in an objective way, fully apart from notions of the countermeasure. When I endeavor to understand a problem, I do not want to bake in assumptions of solutions to the problem statement. That really creates an issue whenever my Action/Solution is less than totally effective. Tracking that back to the original problem can often be the connection that leads to the right solution. We want the ROOT CAUSE(S), NOT SYMPTOMS.

Team / Issue:

OPEN ITEMS TO COMPLETE — Date

Date	Problem / Issue / Opportunity	Action / Solution	Responsible	Date Due	%

Figure 6-4: Open Items to Complete Sheet

What you see here (see figure 6-4) is the Open Items to Complete Sheet. It may appear to be a humble "honey do" listing tool but, in fact, it is so much more. I as an alleged manufacturing engineer dare to make the following statement. Engineers are often guilty of fixing problems on the fly, even on the way to the shop floor. It is borne of having to be efficient. Usually, manufacturing engineers are at a premium and so the few are generally pulled in all directions. I do understand my fellow engineers and am empathetic; but we still must face facts. The Open Items to Complete Sheet helps me to recalibrate the problem solving function inside my head by forcing objectivity. The first column is the "Problems/Issues/Opportunity" column. The discipline here is to write down what the situation is objectively and without any reference to the fix in mind. THERE IS A STRONG TENDENCY FOR FOLKS TO STATE THE OPPORTUNITY IN TERMS OF AN

ALREADY PRECONCEIVED COUNTERMEASURE. "The coolant ain't right." and "Bad drills from the supplier." As opposed to "Duh drill keeps breaking." In other words, document reality - in plain speak. The second column is the "Action/Solution" column. Here is the appropriate place to state the action or countermeasure taken towards fixing the problem. The process of asking the "5 WHYs" happens between the notation of the objective situation and the decision of what to do about it. The action should be driven by this activity.

There are two good reasons for maintaining a mindful separation between the problem and the action. For starters, the invitation is for anyone to address the OITC sheet as an equal resource. *As such, job one is to plainly and without leanings to the solution state the problem at hand.* Anyone who is within touching distance of the process and its operator should be able to do this step- not just problem solvers. The second reason for remaining objective in how the problem is stated on the sheet is that if the fix doesn't work, and the problem is repeating, and then there is a correlating history of the repeats and what didn't work so we can choose differently. The remaining columns on the sheet are to mark who is responsible for the action and when, and finally, status of completion.

Due diligence is a firm requirement of the OITC sheet. One of the golden qualities that this tool has is that someone can tell by simply walking up to the document if it is live or not. One can tell if activity is ongoing and contemporary in that area, or if no one has made and entry or updated an item in months. You can tell if attention has been continuous or intermittent.

The Pre-eminent Visual Control: "GET YOUR RED DOTS HERE!"

Now we have all the elements we need to create the arrangement that you see below. These tools arrayed into a circular affair follow the Deming PDCA model nicely with the added bonus of having a document stand in for each of Deming's points. Each document has its own Future State Behaviors attached to it and together they form a cycle of activities that will actually support Continuous Improvement. AND (here comes my favorite part) as the work is done, as someone is made aware of a problem as it is occurring it gets noted in the "Problem/Issue/Opportunity" column. After 5Ws, the countermeasure ***"SUCH THAT IT NEVER HAPPENS AGAAAIN"*** **(BP)** is noted in the "Action/Solution" column of the OITC sheet. If that action changes the Standard Work, correct or rewrite the document then reset the expectations. There is no additional reporting required. Just use the documents that are posted. Make all relevant notes using my favorite tools: pencil/pen/marker. Then . . . ALL THE

ADMINISTRATIVE WORK IS DONE. RETURN TO WATCHING CYCLE TIME BY TAKT TIME!

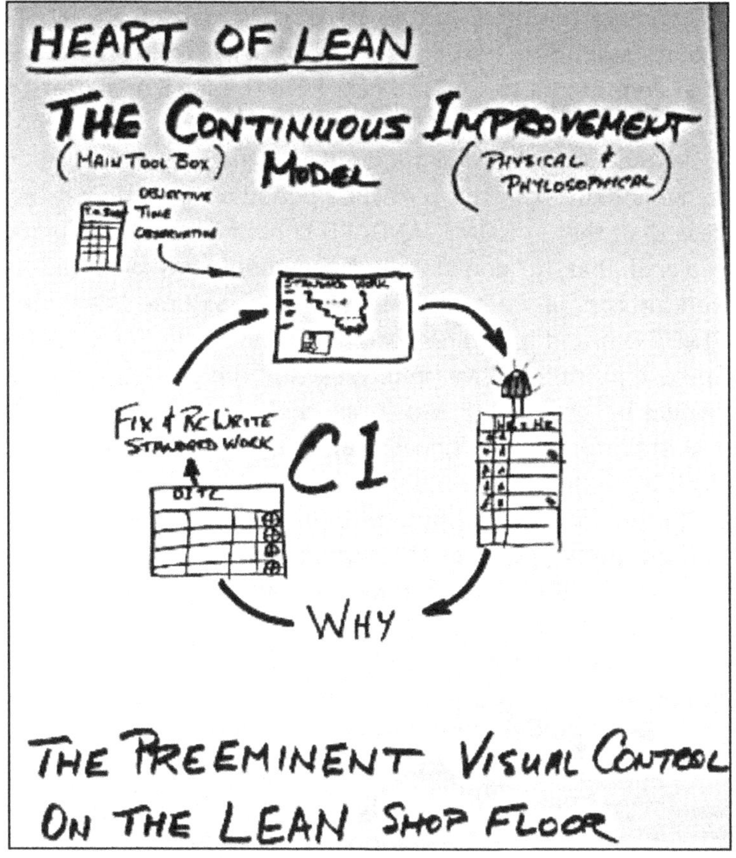

Figure 6-5: Continuous Improvement Model

The arrangements of the documents with respect to PDCA are as follows: Standard Work (via percent load; Takt Time; the customer) gets the 12:00 position and stands for the PLAN. The Hour-by-Hour chart and performing to expectations takes care of the Do part. The Problem/Issue/Opportunity column of the OITC sheet covers the CHECK part and finally, the Action/Solution column with a connection, or feedback loop to supporting or rewriting the Standard Work) supports the ACT part of the model (see figure 6-5). Working together, they form the basis for Basic LEAN Process Management. The array will serve as a super effective Visual Control, while serving to provide a focus for Future State Behavior activity and, most profoundly these tools brought together will facilitate, in real time, in the physical sense, with objective evidence, CONTINUOUS IMPROVEMENT! Finally, Continuous Improvement that you can see! You can tell when last the subject process improved. You can see by how much the process improved along with any pertinent details or history.

There is a primary desirable output of this visual control. RED DOTS! The immediate connotation of a "red dot" is one of negative feedback and as such, the errant goal seems to be to stop red dots from coming. For starters, let's try to understand what a "red dot" is and its value. If time has been apportioned to running a cycle and by Standard Work, we know that we should be able to run that cycle so many times over this particular period of time, then if the output is something less than that, a NON-STANDARD condition arose. SOOoooo... a "red dot" is the signal that a "non-standard" condition has occurred during the Standard Work process. If we have just a little EXCESS time (meaning THE CT IS LESS THAN THE TT) baked into the expectation FOR STUFF TO GO WRONG, then the operator could possibly recover and "make up" the output for that period and everything would be fine, right? Not in an environment where we care about Continuous Improvement! The signal that there is a non-standard condition happening in the middle of a Standard Work process should be viewed as an opportunity. It is a chance to get better at doing what we want to do with that process. **If output always matches the expectation then THERE WILL NEVER BE ANY CONTINUOUS IMPROVEMENT (two exclamation points here)!** You have achieved perfection- a fallacy of forethought to begin with. And based on the description above, how might the value of a red dot be appraised? **In a culture of Continuous Improvement, a red dot is a precious jewel of potential.**

And Bob warns,

"In a culture that is not, it is POISON!"

It is the signal that a better way is possible. It is the roadmap to how to get better, and best yet, red dots are the diagnostic tool that show us what to really work on; what is timely and what is relevant; ALL IN ONE.

The Continuous Improvement Cycle

Continuous Improvement starts with some pre-work. You have to know what all the customers want you to make in the process area and how much of it he wants to buy from you. This leads to the calculation of Takt Time, which is supported by the staffing plan that consumes the average daily time available in the form of CT to support the customer. To get an idea of how much time it DOES take to satisfy the customer you should start writing Standard Work. AND now we're on the board! Plan mathematically how many cycles you can run in each hour's increment given the CT (per the SWCS) that you are running at the time (and NOT the WACT), remembering that some hours there might be a break, or scheduled PM that the operator is responsible for. If you know this much, then you know how many cycles you could run in any given hour. Just write it down for each hour in the split box and add up the accumulated total on the other side of the split. If nothing gets in the way of the operator running the cycle, the output will match the planned side. Maybe your cycle times take many hours or even days to complete. You can still work to expectations. In the case of long cycle times, the primary target is the Takt Time of EACH cycle. If you indeed wrote the Standard Work, then the cycle should break down into "milestones" and you can set daily expectations and adapt the Hour by Hour chart to reflect those Standard Work milestone expectations AND express what time of what day the job should be complete (below left).

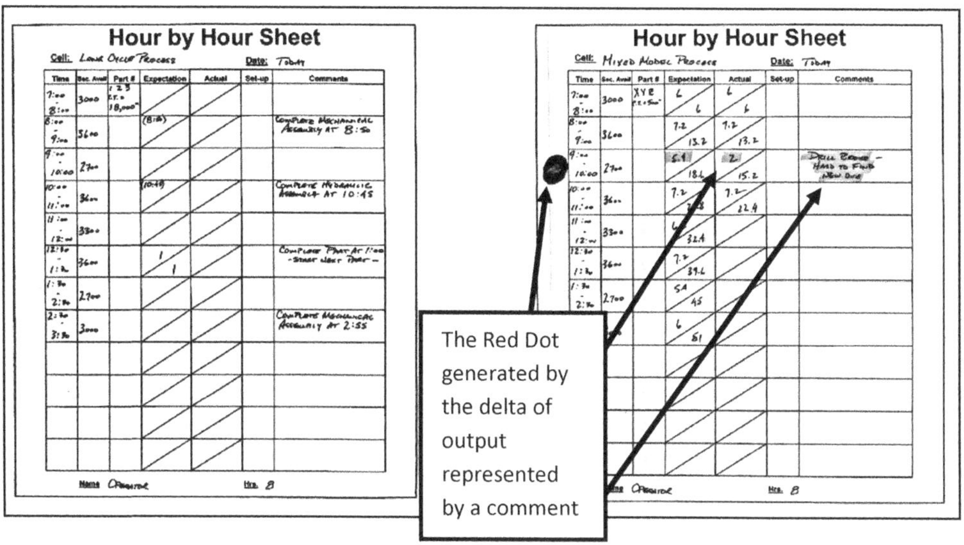

Figure 6-6: Setting Expectations and Generating Red Dots

When things do get in the way (otherwise known as opportunities – and we want a healthy amount of opportunities), there will appear a delta between the actual output and the expectation. AND VIOLA! A RED DOT shows up in the delta between our expectation for between the hours of ____ and ____ AND the actual output (above right: figure 6-6). Since we can see that something moved in and got in the way, we have the opportunity to note the occurrence in the "Opportunities" column and we should be able to gather fairly accurate intel as to what it was that got in the way. I bet the operator still remembers. Get that information down on the Open Items to complete the sheet under "Problem/Issues/Opportunity."

"Toyota wants to understand the FACTS, not the fiction, hence the graduation to visuals every TT or every CT gets us closer to factually understanding 'what got in the way'" **B.P.**

Now, pull together some good folks and ask why it happened. By the way, this idea of 5 Whys is notional. It may take 8, 10 or 15 to get to the ROOT cause, not something superficial. Furthermore, the 5 Whys are not generally linear, with causes and effects laying out end to end. The cause chain will have branches, all branches must be driven to root cause, AND the socio-cultural environment must be such that folks do not take the investigation(s) personally. By the same token, always make it about the process and not about the people, making them "bad" in the situation. Write down the countermeasure(s) that came out of the work that was done asking why under "Action/Solution" and mark the expected completion date. When the fix is in, determine what has to be done to the Standard Work Combination Sheet to make it match the new and improved process and, if necessary, recalculate the output expectations per the new CT. **That would constitute one Continuous Improvement Cycle**. All the documentation one needs to track is left in the wake of the activities at the Visual Control.

"Stop to Fix" (= Andon Lights): The End Game

As explained earlier, the Hour by Hour chart that is used to track performance to the Takt/cycle times of the Standard Work is in danger of quickly becoming a productivity tool if it is not hooked to this little feature; an **Andon** light. This is a sin I have committed in my own travels. If performance to Takt/cycle time is to be used as a Continuous Improvement tool, then the operator must be able to signal at the moment that the operator starts to experience a "Non-Standard" condition in his process (and for the duration, for that matter). The understated power of the Andon light to help create the environment and culture of Continuous Improvement cannot be stressed enough. I have really learned about how powerful it could be in corrective action meetings where the conscientiousness of the operators has come into conversation as it pertained to the contribution of a problem on the shop floor. I have listened to plans made to train conscientiousness into personnel. AND there is my favorite; hoping for someone else "who was just like (blank) used to be, to come along". All too often, I find a glaring absence of anyone knowing when exactly the train left the tracks and what should one really do when that happens. What if (instead of conscientiousness training) we spent time training operators to hit a switch when their train goes off the tracks? A simple switch that was attached to a red flashing light (red for Red Dots!)? Maybe that signal is loud and obnoxious enough to invite attention within a minute of occurrence. Where might that take your processes in terms of Continuous Improvement? Real Time Problem Resolution training? Culture Shift? The Andon light must become an extension of the Visual Control. BIG NOTE HERE>> An extension of the Andon light are the support folks who will be answering the Andon lights. *These folks are the first responders to Non Standard Conditions and they will be driving the credibility of your new Continuous Improvement process.* They don't have to have all the answers to know how to solve the problems, they just have to show up for starters, and they have to first and foremost be able to state a Problem/Issue/Opportunity in objective terms first hand. That's all there is to job one. It doesn't end there but it is a strong place to start.

Continuous Improvement: THE VERB

It seems as though Continuous Improvement is as much activity based as Standard Work is! There is physical structure to engaging in Continuous Improvement and objective evidence as to whether or not you are holding up your end. This begs the question of why it can sound so easy and straightforward and why more companies don't simply do this stuff. There is much to internalize and commit to in the accepting of something new. The notion of Continuous Improvement is itself not at all new, but a real picture of what to do about it and who will need to engage might well be new. It is a picture of what it will take and getting in line is the hardest part. From my experience, once the visual control is in place, once the operator trusts what I am doing there, once I have been able to help him a time or two, a rhythm to the activities will set in and the cylinders will start to fire in earnest: Continuous Improvement physically personified.

"Certainly when something goes amiss it is an opportunity to improve and re-write the SWCS. And, think back to Time Observation. Let us say we have ten elements and five columns-worth of observation. Let us pretend that the CT's are actually 100", 98", 102", 100", and 104." They are all around 100." Let us assume further that there is variation in each of the elemental times observed. If from each element I take the highest task times to write the Standard Work, the CT might be 115." I might never see a red dot. Conversely, if I write the Standard Work using the lowest task times, I will never see a green dot. What is a healthy amount of red dots? What is your problem solving capability and capacity? If it is low and you write the SW too aggressively, everyone will be demotivated. Conversely, if it is lame, the rate of CI will be low and the competition takes our lunch. One of the things I am getting at here is that if you have started out at say a CT of 105," and you "run out of red dots," go back to the TO and choose

more aggressive task times. REMEMBER, YOU ACTUALLY DID OBSERVE THOSE ELEMENTS!" **Bob Pentland**

(Big hint: Never throw Time Observations away. They are one of the most precious forms of work you can do and they keep their value even over time).

Therefore, the discussion would seem to indicate that Continuous Improvement shares a few attributes with that of Standard Work. We have discovered the duality of Continuous Improvement, much the same as Standard Work, in which there is a philosophical notion and origin of the concept, but there also is a huge activity based side to Continuous Improvement as well, just like Standard Work. As such, at the end of the day, Continuous Improvement IS A VERB, just like Standard Work. And there are also Future State Behaviors to support. It has local relevance and personality. You can tell if the CI cycle is turning or if it hasn't turned for some time, just like Standard Work. I would go so far as to say that true Continuous Improvement is an EXTENSION of Standard Work.

CHAPTER 7 - The Playbook

"My Playbook Is Thin"

I learned about all the stuff that has been discussed in the book while working under the tutelage of Mr. Pentland in the days of LEAN transformation at Tuthill Pump in Alsip, Illinois. It was an environment in which practicing LEAN and breaking paradigms was the rule. I wished it would never end. However, one day, it was time for me to leave the nest and face a cold, cruel, LEAN hating, waste loving world of manufacturing. All the tools that we learned about together as well as the principles behind them were swirling about in my head. The feeling of leaving established and functioning LEAN structure that we had taken years to build was scary. I wondered if I would ever find that environment again. I wondered if I could ever influence an organization to take such a leap as to change. I do remember thinking that everyone out there will want this stuff. After all, it works and it's fantastic! Finding another outfit to serve should be easy. In fact, it wasn't really hard to find places that said they were interested in LEAN, but was anyone interested in CHANGING? There were companies out on the frontier that were looking to *do some lean,* or, my personal favorite, had *done some lean* and then let it be. If I was lucky, the smoldering remains of a misguided LEAN initiative could be found out on the shop floor. I have found companies where "someone" in the organization wants to pursue LEAN, but they are alone in it with a similarly lone agenda and don't know what to do about it. And, finally, there were companies whose expectations were simply unrealistic. It feels like I have worked for each of these. Actually, I have.

I don't mean to imply that everyone's LEAN journey will look like this. This one has just been mine. Early on, I had to decide how I was going to represent LEAN in this world of mine. I had to decide how I would approach the different situations that I would encounter. How could I use the different tools that I had learned to handle or even approach these different situations? The fact (for me) is that I did not just figure out how to do that from in the middle of my journey. Rather, I discovered after each time I used LEAN tools and principles to handle or approach a different situation that the string of thoughts and actions I brought to bear were always the same. I was always asking the same (kind of) questions. I was relying on the same tools to document reality and calculate percent loads. AND I used the same Continuous Improvement cycle to watch the process improvements and to help me fix. Through training and several years of developing the muscle memory for it, I find that I had been living my own Standard Work for using the LEAN tools and they lay out just like a *playbook*. I guess that I didn't think of it that way initially because I had always only been exposed to Bob Pentland's delivery of the LEAN message. He was able to influence the WANT of the material from the Chief in Charge perspective or from the consultant to (paying) client perspective. In the early days of his consulting, he used to tell us that he doesn't work for companies (clients) he works for people. I think that meant that without reaching the WANTS of an actual person, LEAN never has a good chance to gain traction in any company. This also helps me understand how most LEAN books are written to speak to high level people, whose WANTS could be ignited for the greater good of a company, to have the influence to initiate change. It is a necessity. However, life for me has not always resembled this. I have not always had access to the people in an organization that have influence over the direction of the company, OR, those people were being influenced by something they wanted more- some sacred cow (like the new ERP system that they convinced corporate to spend a bazillion dollars on). Sometimes I have taken jobs as one of the nameless rabble, just trying to stay employed. That is an interesting position to try to push a LEAN message from, let me tell you, but I often found a way. This approach of using LEAN tools to help with problems and then promoting from underneath came to be known in my own mind as "LEAN trench fighting". Anyway, in any of the employment scenarios that I was dealing with, I came to realize that, when it came to LEAN, I was working from a very thin playbook; a reliable, trustworthy playbook - razor thin.

Playbook for LEAN Trench Fighters

I admitted that I made up the phrase "LEAN trench fighter" as a cross between a journey descriptor and a persona that I indulge occasionally, but it does describe what it's like when you are the only one in the "room" who believes in something (same room the proverbial elephant is in, I suppose). Such has now and again been the case, I found myself in a new position. That is one really good reason I am glad I am a manufacturing engineer (allegedly); gives me something to start with. The infection of LEAN has always been in me since Tuthill, though, and every time I approached a process based problem, the tools of LEAN would naturally come to my fingers and through the tools, I would come to SEE things clearly; to see through the hysterical data and to get in contact with reality. The LEAN tools, used for problem solving always produce a diary of documents that always, first and foremost, bring me comfort that I understood the problem. Adhering to the LEAN documents also always provides me with a clear record of what I was doing so when solving a problem is difficult or has many tentacles, I can keep track of what I have done. Finally, using the LEAN tools means that I can typically create an expectation of the outcome of whatever I have changed, fixed, removed, etc. What better controls could there be for solving process based controls?

This last part is my favorite: as mentioned before, going through the above efforts produces a diary of wonderful documents that instantly become tools to communicate, promote or even train the concepts of the process change or problem resolution. For instance, showing and reading the Standard Work of the newly documented process to the process operator seems like a highly practical activity to me. Process operators love LEAN documents and I have never had trouble engaging shop floor folks with LEAN docs. They make so much sense that a process operator can follow what is going on with, say, a Percent Load chart or a Standard Work Combination Sheet and Standard Work Sheet. They will typically be impressed that someone stood there and watched, with attention to detail, what the operator did, let alone documented it with accuracy and understanding, although, they will never know if you don't talk to them about it, so, use it to promote.

Standard Work and Welding Cyclonic Thingies

I had such an opportunity in 2011 while I was working as a manufacturing engineer for an outfit that took new heavy truck chassis and made them into water maintenance equipment – like a big shop vac. I was there to support 128 shop floor employees in the assembly building who installed the hydraulics, electrical, and weldments that assembled onto these new truck chassis became the product. The weldments were manufactured upstream through laser cutting, welding and machining departments, then delivered to the assembly building (after a compulsory stop through the warehouse). The larger components were made to order and not stocked as inventory (except for one day; reference compulsory stop).

One reoccurring problem we had in the assembly building was that if large components were not completed and delivered on time, much of the truck build would have to stop because it was impossible to work around the missing component. One such component resembled a cyclonic vacuum cleaner body. Two of these were welded side by side. The cycle time to make one of these little numbers (which finished out at about 6 feet tall and a quarter ton) was historically 18 hours and could only be welded by this one guy, "who was difficult to work with". This turned out to be just a rumor (I later found the gentleman to be quite a nice man). He was the only one who had been doing it for almost the last 10 years. The last thing anyone wanted to do was upset him because if he wanted to take his marbles and go home, well, that would be the end of the cyclonic thingies. And still, my guys couldn't get one on time to save their build schedules. I decided to walk up and meet this welder. Sure enough, he was kind of a biker type, and a bigger fella than myself. He didn't bite me, though. I guess I was kind of a curiosity to him. I asked if he minded if I stood with him through the whole process of making a cyclonic thingy. He told me that nobody had ever suggested such a thing and he warned that this takes time and it isn't clean or pretty back here. I told him I understood the ramifications of my hanging out and away we went.

I also asked him if I could document what he was doing and he asked me if I was going to do a "time study". I said, "No. I don't do 'time studies'. I do 'Time Observations'". I explained the distinction being that I won't add or subtract any elements that I observe (that we don't discuss and decide on together), and that I will represent the document as it really happened without judgment. The operator was completely agreeable to those terms (as I believe almost all operators have been in my experience). I secured a welding mask and jacket and stood by my welding man while he did his thing. For starters, we could not make 18 hours of continuous work out of making a cyclonic thingy, but he spent at least that in elapsed time, as his parts stores were chronically empty. These were NOT supposed to be made to order components, but regularly stored parts so he could make any cyclonic thingy variation at any time. However, their replenishment was predicted by an MRP program and it was currently releasing welding work before it released laser cutting of plate. This guy knew that, so he would go appeal to the laser area supervisor who would sometime move the cutting in his schedule to help. By the time the welder was done expediting his own material, it took 18 hours (at least) to make one.

We determined which unit order he had all the components for so we could actually see the process of creating a cyclonic thingy and the time observation began. At the end of the day, we could not make 8 hours out of welding together one of these units. AND, at one point, I observed him tacking together parts for fit in the main unit body, only to cut them back apart to allow them to flex and articulate into the body of the assembly (due to design), then re-weld it all back together. We (meaning just the two of us) discussed options and decided that if the one plate on top were made of two then they could be parted for fitting and then brought together for welding like a clamshell. We made the suggestion to design engineering and they liked it. The 8-hour cycle time became much closer to six. I wrote the Standard Work (see figures 7-1 and 7-2).

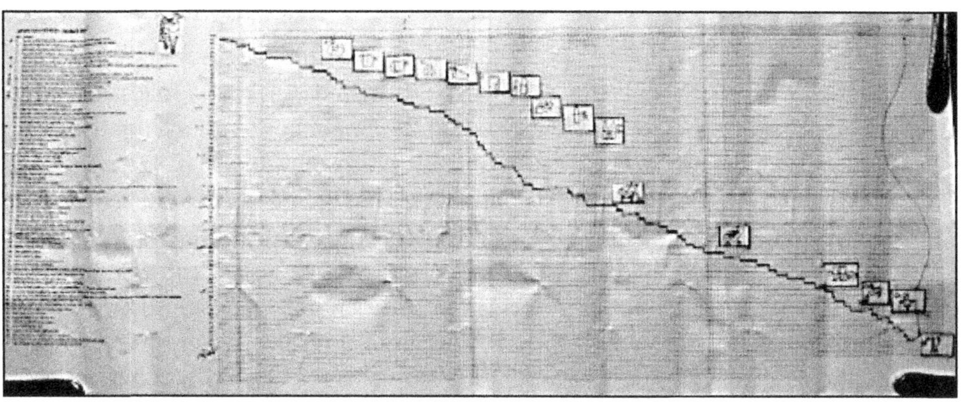

Figure 7-1: Welding Standard Work

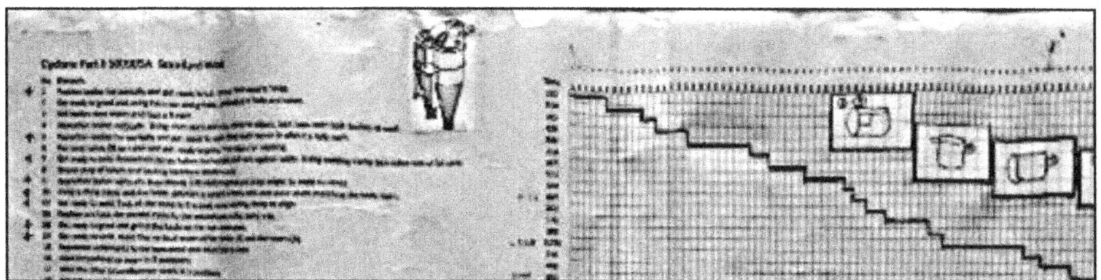

Figure 7-2: Welding Standard Work Close Up

The company was not interested in the document; they were interested in the time standard, which they changed from 18 hours to eight (weren't gutsy enough to go for the 6). The operator and I kept the Standard Work. We weren't done with it. Unbeknownst to the organization, this welder absolutely hated this job, but he always had to do it because there was a perception that only he could do it correctly. He wanted to train someone else. We made a deal with the weld shop supervisor that the next welder hired would be that trainee. Later that week, the company hired a couple of brothers with just better than entry-level MiG welding skills. We used the Standard Work Combination Sheet to train those two brothers. It took only about 5 to 6 repeats for both of them to be able to do it without coaching. My welder friend was reassigned to help out in another area where his talents were better utilized (and he was much happier). He handed the Standard Work back to me as he transferred. I was unable to get the company to follow Standard Work, but that fella understood, and he used it to help himself and the company.

Playbook for the Facility Manager

I have come to feel that the only real differences in the application of a playbook approach from LEAN application to LEAN management lies mostly in the resolution. As it pertains to LEAN, the subject of resolution is really connected with the overarching goal at hand. Operations Management is likely wanting to explore the idea of a "LEAN Operating System" (I hope): that is to say, a comprehensive replacement for their current operating system that is wasteful and doesn't work well. At some point, the leader is going to have to be able to draw a model to emulate or shoot for. The LEAN Operating System really begins with just the assembly of the tools and visual controls that have been discussed in the previous chapters; one per process operator, and not just for the sake of doing so. Folks need to work to set up non-wasteful processes that the company can be successful with first. Then, as we discussed, the Continuous Improvement Cycle works off of the tools displayed on the visual control. The cycles run and the results are marked. Red Dots are addressed and problems are fixed. The cycle is supported or improved and round and round we go, executing and checking each elemental line of the Standard Work Combination Sheet, each cycle, each Takt Time. This is a very physical, visual action occurring- call it ground floor to plus 5,000 feet. Now pan out to 20,000 feet. If a manager had several areas that were doing the same thing, running cycles, comparing them with the expectations and instantly reporting if the process goes into a non-standard condition, then it would be like each cycle of each Takt Time is an element of an overall Standard Work Combination Sheet representing the cycling of an enterprise level Takt Time. This image is a bit conceptual but the signals and the chances to ask "**why**" when things go wrong are very real. The point I am trying to make is that the "standard / non-standard condition" indicators of all the manufacturing cells of an organization can generate enterprise level Red Dots and the opportunity to understand and fix them in real time exists.

"As a note, my teachers ALWAYS referred to them as 'flows', cells were something 'you put an animal in in.'" **B.P. (As per Mr. Nakoa)**

Continued success to the company's plan can be monitored. The plan-do-check-act nature of the cycle still exists and the same actions to a Red Dot can be taken. An enterprise level visual control to track and work to that looks like the one in the Continuous Improvement chapter could be created and now we're cooking at 20,000 feet.

Fishbones and Cryogenic Vessels

I created such a system when I was plant manager for a small company that made cryogenic vessels for the scientific community in 2012. I had about 25 welders, machinists and assemblers plus a few utility folks. The units we made were usually one to four off and had manufacturing cycle times typically of weeks to months across welding, machining components, final assemblies and testing, and outside services. With payment milestones sprinkled along each time line, this little company often "lived close to the vest" towards the coming incremental paydays and the shop had to make those milestones. The manufacturing processes were described in "travelers" that the design engineer would type up and cost estimate against for each individual project. There were typically 8 to 12 such projects running through the shop at any given time. I needed a way to SEE if I was on track or if I was biting it; a thing I at the time could NOT see coming or worse - happening. What I decided to do was to find a way to represent all those projects together as elements of the same Standard Work Combination Sheet. I scrounged around and found several rolls of old adding machine paper. I decided that I could use that to translate the project process travelers into "fishbone" type charts, with the operation steps (welding, machining, and assembly) scaled to time. I stacked parallel operations and represented outside ops as the "bones" coming into the fishbone – again scaled to time. I also created an 8-foot-by-8-foot field of corkboard facing out into the manufacturing floor to place my fishboned projects on and it had the same time scale across the top of it as the fishbones were made to: 8 feet represented approximately 2.5 months of time. Now, I could put the fishbone charts up with the project target finish dates lined up with the corresponding finish date on the corkboard's time/date scale. Now I could read down vertically at all the tasks stacked on any one week and tell if any of my departments were over committed or if any were running out of work. I could also see the outside service requirements coming before the day I even needed them and I could call to check in to see that there would be no surprises. And at the end of each day/week, I had red dots to ask why about. Those red dots weren't just points of failure; they were data points right off the Standard Work cycle that could be fixed.

Approach to Project Work

As a LEAN trench fighter (again, my head – my term), I have been called upon to lead projects and I have had to solve problems. My playbook for either activity is the same, and do you know what? It is very thin!

The classic 5-day Kaizen Event structure follows the Plan Do Check Act nature of the Continuous Improvement Cycle and serves as a wonderful model from which to navigate all projects. For starters, the trusty A3 charter could be considered the Standard Work for a typical Kaizen type project: An intention is stated; relevant reality is documented; scope is identified; goals for the project week are issued, and the team works to meet the Kaizen Week goals. In Kaizen Events that I have worked on (over 200 formally chartered ones), we would keep track of daily goals and activities on Open Items to Complete Sheets and every day there was a leaders' meeting at the end to check in with those daily goals. Adjustments were then made to get the project week back on schedule. Recalibrations of goals are made if necessary.

If an organization sets up and runs a couple of Kaizen type events in this way, and there are challenges in the midst of the first few Kaizen weeks, you can use the cycle of the week to identify where trouble began and fix it to get better at you rapid improvement skills. Make no mistake, the problem probably had nothing to do with the actual problem at hand, but had to do with how the event was supported. Did you go into the event week without enough maintenance support? Were the process experts not included in the team roster? Was it perceived that the event would "cost" too much to take certain people out of action to participate in? No matter with any of these problems if you are running the event week by the Continuous Improvement model, because the shortfall will be exposed and the opportunity to learn from and fix happens each time any issue comes up throughout the week. An organization can get really proficient at setting up and conducting successful and profitable project weeks using the playbook.

Daily Project Cycling During a Kaizen Event

In 2000, I experienced a really good example of setting up a Kaizen week by the application template to get better at working a "KAIZEN WEEK". I was part of a corporate wide training program when I worked at Tuthill. A couple of folks from each of the business units would descend on a Tuthill factory and do a Kaizen Week in which we would all rotate into the position of Team Leader. The facilitator was one of Bob Pentland's consulting partners, Craig Robbins. He too had spent time learning from the O.G. senseis of Shingijutsu. That week, Craig used an interesting twist to the Open Items to Complete Sheets that each Kaizen Team was using to plan-do-check and-act through their respective Kaizen week. He asked us each day (whoever the team leader was going to be that day) to use one color for all that they write until 10:00 am, to switch to a second color to be used until noon, to switch to a third color to be used until 2:00 pm and to switch to a fourth color for use for the rest of the day. It took a day or two, but once we had been at it and had one or two days of Open Items on our sheets, it was plain to see that there was generally very little writing in the second color, but a big increase in the color just before the Leaders Meeting. That pointed to a soft period of action for our team and that period was the late morning period. It seems that we would engage in analysis paralysis during that time, as the pressure of the coming Leaders Meeting at the end of the day was not pushing us to perform, get things done. We decided to move clean-up of yesterday's Open Items to that period to squeeze the time we had to make option-decisions on open items to act upon. Craig explained to us that by changing colors, we were able to communicate the cadence of the process of the project in visual terms. Essentially, Craig took a five day Kaizen Event (itself, one cycle of a sort) and delineated five discreet cycles for us to run and look for opportunities to improve.

Approach to Problem Solving

Approaching a specific problem out on the shop floor works just the same way for me to my mind. In this case, I am initially interested in the actual process Standard Work and how stable it is to begin with. I don't rely on hysterical data for this intel. I go observe. After the existing Standard Work is identified, I look for where the problem exists within the context of the Standard Work. Only then can I see if something changed or if something had remained unfixed. Whatever the case, something is unfixed now, so asking why and fixing is next. Then reestablish the Standard Work to support the process complete with fix in place and new expectations to expose problems. If the change impacts the Percent Load, then that must be rationalized as well so the customer is supported. Lather; Rinse; Repeat.

Problem Resolution by Fixing Element Order

We use Standard Work in problem resolution all the time where I work now. Here is one such example recently. We have been making aluminum manifold blocks, which are a pain to inspect for burrs between connecting holes. Our operators would occasionally let something go through that had a hanging burr in cross-holes, and typically, the order was to increase inspection awareness. After the failure of the operators, an inspection "gate" activity was tacked on to the process routing. Problem was that no two inspectors looked the parts over in exactly the same way. I set out to do a time observation and write the Standard Work on an inspector looking over the part. No sooner than I finished writing the Standard Work, I watched the inspector violate the sequence. I asked why and he said he wasn't aware that he had altered the process path. What was happening was that the process dictated that a visual inspection of all external machined surfaces be done and then to look at these two critical shallow counter bores to be burr free but not to exceed a critical .01 max edge break. That was how the steps were written, but because the inspector understood the need to look at the counter bores, he would be drawn to them whenever catching sight in the handling of the part. After that, the inspector would often forget to finish the visual inspection of externally milled features. We discussed it and decided that the shallow counter bores should be the first thing to look at and it should be assumed that they will need touching with fine Scotch Brite. After that, the inspector can run through the visual of all external milled features without distraction. It did not take long before we discovered that if an inspector could "learn" to inspect a specific part, that so could the original operator. Guess who first uses the Scotch Brite on the counter bores and then checks the visual attributes now, as the Standard Work is specifically written.

A Playbook for Administrative Processes

Administrative processes can be improved just the same and using the same (kind) of tools as value adding processes. Admin processes bear a few differences from value adding processes in that they are not always linear; they sometimes take place over a period of time but their process is not continuous or the time not well defined; they are one of a number of admin processes taking place in front of the process operator. Writing the Standard Work for an administrative process is best done using Process Mapping. This is not a new concept and several computer programs are already dedicated to process mapping like Visio or modules within Excel and Word. However, I much prefer using sticky notes, butcher paper and yarn. These are the tools that Mr. Pentland taught us process mapping with. Don't need a computer; all in the room can participate. ***"PER TOYOTA, THESE ARE STRUCTURES FOR DIALOGUE"*** **(B.P.)** The rules for LEAN Process Mapping are simple: Use the rows to depict different people in the process; time flows from left to right – do your best to make the sticky notes follow the time; include a timeline description underneath (depicting breaks or jumps as needed). These rules emulate how we fill out a Standard Work Combination Sheet and doing so will mean that you have written Standard Work for an Administrative Process. Now there is nothing left to do but RUN the process and observe if it runs to the expectation or if issues pop up. When issues do pop up, the most important thing would be to be able to SEE IT HAPPEN! WHEN IT HAPPENS! How could one be assured of seeing a Red Dot at the moment of occurrence (or as close to as possible)? And if we fix a Red Dot, will it impact our process map and process cycle time? Have we still supported the customer OR are we better able to support the customer (an administrative process customer may be an internal customer). The latter would be wonderful. Continuous Improvement AND a reduction of cost- especially when you consider that it is quite likely that your admin processes don't add value (some admin processes ARE the value stream, I understand. Forgive me; I am just a metal head).

Process Mapping the "ROM" Quote

I was able to use the tools to help with a situation in 2012, working as an Advanced Manufacturing Engineer. I had not worked there very long and I soon became aware of a perceived problem by the sales force. They felt that they could never get a quote through the AME (new product quoting) department. They would wait for word of whether the company was interested in a package that the salesperson had brought for us to look at and not hear a word or it would just take a terribly long time. This was interesting in that one of the other AMEs kept up a huge APQP-esque log. It had at least 30 columns of items that are (or might) come into play in the course of a committed cost quote. The deliverables for all these log items came from different people and had the AME always chasing for answers from these folks so he could fill in the box on the log. The VP of Operations finally articulated the aforementioned problem (can't get a quote out of the AMEs) and asked us to do something. We scheduled a meeting. As the new guy, and working from ignorance, I asked what the process currently IS. I knew this meeting might be an opportunity to use some of the LEAN tools so I had packed a supply of colorful sticky notes and a roll of plotter paper. The other AMEs described the existing process complete with the list of players and intended old school timeline of 20 working days. I arranged a process map based on what they told me and viola! We had existing Standard Work. Just by comparing the events of the last few quoting iterations with the intended process laid out on paper, we could easily tell two things: 1) we would routinely lose the timeline to activities we did not control like quoting fixtures and castings, AND 2) (this one's a bit of a too-fer) the customer did not always need a "committed cost quote" (almost never), but they did need some information in much less time than 20 working days (almost always). As we discussed the process map and the red dots of the previous few quotes, we discovered that as it pertained to parts of the process that we controlled, like estimating tool path, we could have that finished in days, sometime hours. However, trying to get a quote out of a large foundry for tooling and pours for parts EAU of 500 per year wasn't going to hit the top of their priority list and could sometimes take even more than 20 working days. We decided that with those tasks that we had control over, we could routinely turn a quote around in 5 working days. We even learned how to quote fixturing to within about 6-8% consistently (that part actually takes about 30-60 seconds these days). We wrote the new Standard Work (in process map form complete with timeline) and we call them ROM quotes; "Rough Order of Magnitude" and customers can have a ROM quote in 5 working days.

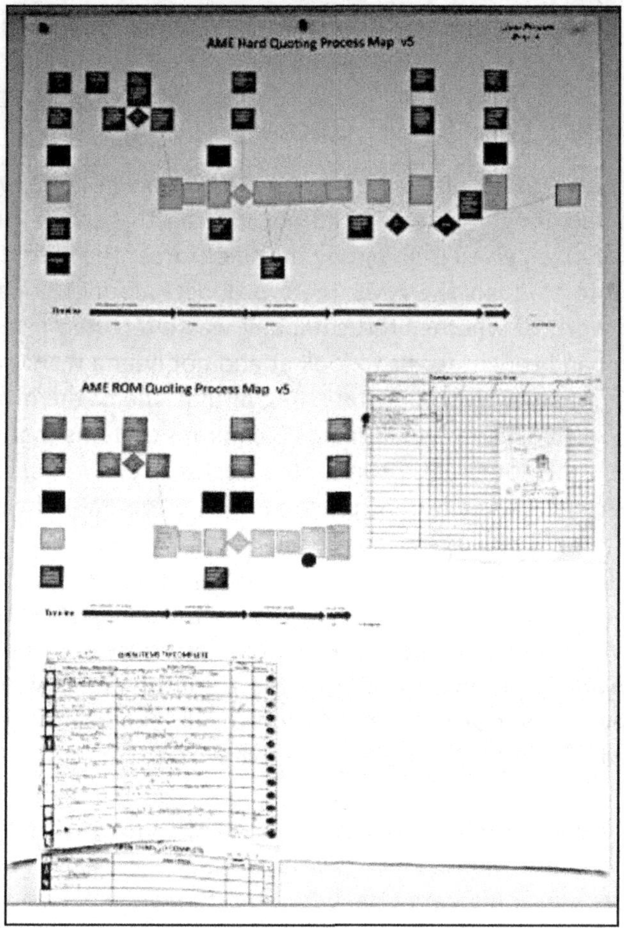

Figure 7-3: AME Process Maps

The process maps hang in my office on the wall (see figure 7-3) and I maintain a much simpler log to support it. Notice that the committed quote process map is hanging above the new ROM type and still represents the valid process if committed quote costs are what is needed by the customer. We found that this level of detail was more pertinent at the end of the quoting process. These days, buyers are looking for the ballpark and so are we. If, cost wise, we are not in the same area code, we want to spend our resources elsewhere. We can now tell if we are in the same ballpark within 5 working days. I collect red dots and ask why when they come along. You can see them on the Open Items to Complete Sheets hanging below my Standard Work.

Did I Say My Playbook Is Thin?

Yes I did! At this point, I would hope that all the above examples are starting to sound like they follow the same path. They should. They all have identical themes. In a very few cases, the tools may look slightly different, but in all cases their natures and intents are just the same. They create a Stable Playbook! It doesn't matter if you are using it on the shop floor, in an office process or to manage and area. Let me state the elements generically:

>> What is going on – really?

This goes back to documenting reality and that means (ultimately) time observation of the actual process in action (value added or administrative), executed with detail and discipline. This step happened in each anecdotal case above. I had to go to where the welding was taking place and watch. I had to document the current quoting process.

>> Document if possible – return to start if not

Write the Standard Work if not written. We have discussed the idea of not arbitrarily writing in undesirable elements into our Standard Work just for the sake of getting it done. Sometimes, it is important to document the process as is, especially when complicated problem solving is in process. Use the writing of Standard Work as an indicator of a stable process. If the process is stable, then writing the Standard Work will not be a problem. If you can't seem to write the Standard Work, then go create an actual process for you to start with. It's that simple.

Each of the examples has a Standard Work attribute as well. Some of them look just a little different; the welding and the aluminum block inspection Standard Works were written on a Standard Work Combination Sheet just like the one described in the tools section, but I had to come up with the fishbone format when I was trying to imagine and describe the weeks long cycles of one off jobs. The ROM Quoting example used a standard Process Map to describe Standard Work.

>> Identify opportunities in context to the Standard Work

You are using your playbook for a reason. What is it? Are you there to fix something that isn't working? Are you trying to manage a process or collection of processes? Whatever the case, if you can SEE the Standard Work cycling, you should be able to see where and when opportunities occur within those cycles. Craig Robbin's use of time based color schemes to using Open Items to Complete Sheets during Kaizen weeks actually served to expose the "cycle" of daily behavior so we could SEE the cadence of our effort.

>> Fix what needs fixing without destroying the rest of the working Standard Condition

The very idea of having Standard Work in the forefront of any problem solving campfire discussions ensures that we will not end up firing in all directions as can often be the case, especially if the problem is an elusive one. If Standard Work was written, then there is a good chance that much of the Standard Work is quite serviceable and should be preserved and protected. Learn to SEE the offending elements among the more stable, value adding elements.

In the Quoting example above, once we could see all the elements and identify those that routinely gave up the heartburn, we saw something very interesting: all the elements that we could control, we could perform in hours or days. Those happened to be the very elements that (upon taking the customer's perspective) were most important to a "rapid response" quote and by reordering the quoting elements to only include what we could control, we could have a quote response within 5 days consistently.

>> Cycle the new process and continue to look for opportunities to improve

Then, after all that happens, what happens next? It is our first chance to SEE the new cycle as it runs and to SEE if it runs flawlessly or if it produces a Red Dot – cycling over and over again, with the idea that we WANT to SEE that next opportunity to get better at doing it.

Once committed to a Standard Work understanding, ALL the above examples were turned on like engines and allowed to CYCLE. And with the repetition of cycles, the Red Dots would come. The opportunities would come.

These steps and the tools that support the actions do line up into a playbook that I have relied on like a wise old friend. I have used this approach for all types of situations and especially ones that have an element of the unknown; no preconceived notions of what the real problem is; no practical idea what to do about what we don't understand; no idea where to go from here. Friends and colleagues have mentioned to me in the past how I seem to like dealing with issues that have dark corners and unknown vistas to them. The reality is that I don't particularly *like* the stressful unknown of that kind of situation. However, I DO like how my playbook lights up the way. I LOVE showing people wasteful stuff that has been happening all along without any understanding, and right under our noses. It always blows minds and is the very best promotional devise ever!

The LEAN practitioner would do well to develop this approach by developing the muscle memory of it, which means practice it every chance you get. You can begin by doing it with your own job. I have Standard Work for quoting new business as an Advanced Manufacturing Engineer (my *real* current job). When the company decided that 20 working days to a quote was too slow, we reworked the process in a Kaizen sort of way and now the Standard Work says 5 days and I compare each quote with that outcome expectation. Once, in times of company austerity, we did our own housekeeping in the office area and I was the vacuum tech. I wrote my Standard Work (SWCS and SWS of the office floor space) and performed to it on the appointed intervals. I continuously improved (which meant I reduced the number of times I had to plug and unplug, etc.) and proved that twice per week kept things tidy, even in the winter (tracking salt on black carpet). The boys all thought it was great fun to watch me go through the gyrations of keeping a visual control for vacuuming the floor but little did they know I was actually training them! Some of them actually engaged in real time problem resolution, as I would manage to suck up their tangles of computer wires or rediscover old utensils under their desks.

One of my great hopes in presenting my own journey such as it has been is to communicate the idea that LEAN can live as an ember within the folks that have truly internalized it. It is an ember that can be fanned back to flame on demand. Failure modes are always themselves the precious Red Dots that provide the opportunity to "Do It Better" (fill in your own "It"). I also hope and sincerely believe that the perspective of LEAN trench fighter "translates up." What I mean is that my journey has been an exercise in "what it takes." Doing LEAN things in the midst of some of the varied situations I have encountered has often had to serve as its own reward for me, and in that, I think it served to solidify my vision of the LEAN end game: to operate waste free; self / visually managed flows of cash value. As levels of involvement, management, technology, proximity, and time spent, radiate up and away from the actual location of value adding activity, the less influence on any continued LEAN journey that person or activity will have. I don't believe that some of the more classically, philosophically presented LEAN teachings, which were angled to compel industry leaders who can make the decisions to follow a LEAN journey always "translate down" very well. Those books don't always effectively tap the "what it takes" component; or as importantly, the "WHO IT TAKES" to get it done. Somebody has to live these tools in order for a LEAN system to work. Maybe we all need a little LEAN trench fighter in us to create the ember of belief – and want. Now, the executive fuel from above will provide a LEAN initiative with sustained energy to flourish instead of just flame out, crash and burn.

CHAPTER 8 - More Stories From the Frontier

More of My "Thin Playbook"

I always love story time. Bob calls them my "homey stories" and I take that as a term of endearment and a nod to my LEAN tenacity. But let me make this perfectly clear: I have never done anything more than just apply these few fundamental tools into a patterned approach that has consistently lead me to where I wanted to go LEAN-wise. Often times, I have had no real idea of what I was going to find. Here is a promise of this process that I have been comfortable giving in the last ten years of my career: "I don't know what exactly we will find/see, but I know that we'll know what to do when we finally find/see it."

I have often said, "Document reality, apply the tools, and I never know where it will take, and, always to a place of goodness". B. Pentland

It is my internal promise to myself and it has not let me down, but it is a heady promise to give to, say, a project group, or maybe the president of your company when things are going wrong. My introduction to Engineering in American manufacturing was to believe that it was better to know the answer going into the question, but I don't believe that anymore. I have often found/seen so much more of the problem through the application of the Standard Work / Continuous Improvement playbook than ever I have by just treating symptoms, and I suspect that is what happens when we just rush in at a problem without an open mind (as though it won't make time for us again, later).

I have been very fortunate to have jobs that allowed me the opportunity to deal with a varied list of problems over my tenure as a manufacturing engineer. It has also been my good fortune to find myself in the company of others (along with myself) that have no preconceived clue as to what to do about it. That is a wonderful place to start from. I have just a few more stories that came out of just such situations in my past; my homey stories. I really treasure them all and the best of it is- you can't make this stuff up.

Resolving Random Motion Activity and the Oil Filter Housings

In 2008, I was working as the "Process Development Manager" for an outfit that made large machined weldments as a tier one supplier for a major equipment manufacturer. In this case, we were dealing with large oil filter housings for big 8 and 12 cylinder generator motors. The Red Dot was that we would weld and machine these things by the piles and then they would collect in front of a manual deburring operation, where all the sharp edges generated in machining were eliminated. The specification for the item to be burr AND WELDBERRY free (weld berries are from welding spatter) was stringent as this was an engine component exposed to the internal workings and the customer was quite vigilant on this point. Perfect parts (dimensionally) with a single missed weld berry or flappy Klingon chip were losers- 100%. The operators who typically did the deburring were lower on the scale of pay than welders or machinists, so they were usually those folks with a little less time and experience than the average employee. We had no real idea of how much time it should take and there certainly was no Standard Work. There was only Jimmy. Jimmy did it good. Jimmy did it fast. We didn't see as many rejections when Jimmy did it. Jimmy was a nice young fella who wasn't afraid to work hard. When he first came to work for the company, they started him out deburring and he probably did a mountain of oil filter housings over some time. Whatever method he worked through, in the end, his deburring was preferred over anyone else's. The problem was that Jimmy was a very worthwhile young man and he had potential. He wanted to grow past deburring parts and learn to do jobs that paid better (makes perfect sense). The last thing we wanted to do was move Jimmy out of deburring, but right is right and Jimmy demonstrated that he was ready to grow, so move him we did.

The remaining deburring talent had experience and they were familiar with the stringent goal of NO burrs or weld berries, but there methods varied dramatically AND unfortunately, so did their results, both in terms of quality and cycle time. It seemed that the only successful processes took an average of 2.5 times the cycle time to deburr as Jimmy used to take. It was said that they were turning the oil filter housings into "Cadillacs", as they were polished to a fine shine (over processing!). One thing is for sure; WE weren't getting PAID to make Cadillacs. The job to figure this out became mine, and guess what; I had no idea what to do about it (surprise!). That is not entirely true. I had a Playbook.

Jimmy had moved on to a position where he loaded welding robots, so he was still among us (in proximity of the deburring operation). I asked if he would please spend some time with me while I watched him deburr some oil filter housings. He asked me if this would result in his having to come back and permanently deburr those things forever. I told him to the contrary that it would ensure that he would effectively be able to finally pass the torch and not have to deburr housings again forever (but never say never). He agreed and I did a Time Observation. Jimmy's method wasn't perfect, but you could see the process in it as he tried to move the large part (about 8" diameter x 32" long) to each aspect once and then rotate the deburring tools. He also had a couple of tools designed to make it possible to reach into some cavities more easily. They were simple, effective and easily duplicated. Jimmy and I discussed just a few amendments to how to move the part and the tooling selection, after which, I wrote the Standard Work for a cycle time of 884". I used simple pictures to depict how the part should lay for each section of the Standard Work and these served as an assist to the "Standard Work Sheet" component. I thanked Jimmy and told him that I wished him well as a welding robot loader.

The very next thing that I did was to call in the supervisor who the deburring folks reported to. He was a good fella and was open to whatever might help him in this situation. (He had been one of the main proponents of Jimmy's leaving to grow, but it stinks to do the right thing and be bitten by it.) I took the Standard Work Combination Sheet and put it in his hands. Then we read it aloud once through and then again as I moved the part in the same ways as the SWCS said. The supervisor was then given all the tools and PPE and asked to try to perform the work as he just heard it. In his first attempt, he deburred a part in 955" and it was burr and weld berry free. I did an element-by-element audit directly on the Standard Work Combination Sheet to show it. (This is one of my favorite things to do. The objective evidence of having validated the process becomes a part of the document, and it looks loved. See the before and after figure 8-1 pictured below).

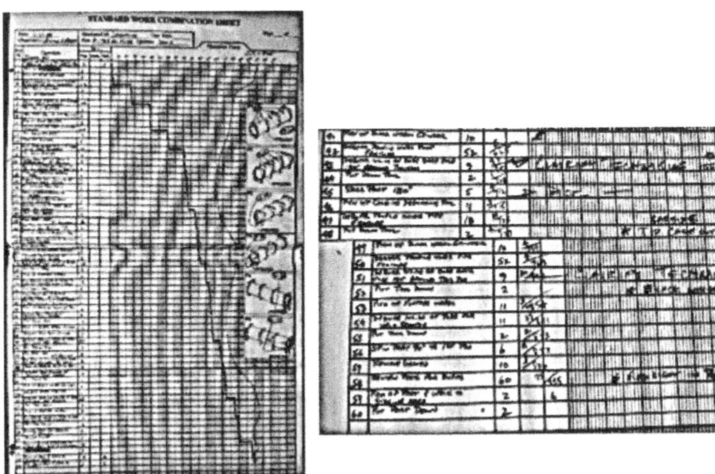

Figure 8-1: Deburring Standard Work

Within four attempts, he was within 10" to 15" of Jimmy's time (the Standard Work) and producing to the quality expectation. We then duplicated that process with our remaining deburring talent and had the same results. No more piles.

Using Autonomation to Fix the Missing Hole

Shingijutsu defined Autonomation (or Jidoka in Japanese) as the observation of the combination of human work elements alongside the machine cycles as being a Standard Work Cycle. Autonomation creates a condition where quality is built into the process and it prevents the reoccurrence of abnormal conditions. That sounds great. Every manager should decree that autonomation should prevail throughout the land! This concept is pretty deep despite its rather simple composition. It really requires relating a physical experience to convey what autonomation really LOOKS like.

I have used it on several occasions in the name of problem resolution. On one occasion recently, we had a Red Dot (a rather serious one) in a cell that supplies a mixed model family of parts to a major customer and we sent a part without the "bypass hole" being drilled in it. This cell has four discreet machines in it and some post processing steps all in the following order: two lathes machining; a drill press-drill the hole; deburr bench; inspection bench; the stamping machine-stamp the number; and finally the finished cart. The Standard Work for the process had been written and remained quite stable for over two years AND NOW we made a part without the bloody hole in it.

The Red Dot made it to the "corrective action meeting," which was the current problem resolution process in the organization. The meeting was always held in a conference room and had a long distinguished history of being a great way to burn an hour. A cross functional panel of experts decided that the corrective action for this problem would be to require a zip-tie to be put through the hole of each part in process (for the customer to have to remove) to prove that it has a hole in it (hence the "can't make this stuff up" comment). I decided to go out and watch what the operator was doing.

When I got there, I picked up the Standard Work Combination Sheet and could follow along with what the operator was actually doing for the first few cycles (see figure 8-2). Then something happened. In the second machine, a critical bore was held to +/- .001 of an inch. As the machine would warm up in the day or as the tool would wear, that bore would have to be adjusted in the machine's offset register. Not wanting to proceed in his process without verifying that the critical bore was back in spec, the operator would wait for the part to be finished and then take it past the drill press to the inspection bench to check it out – *AND*

THERE IT WAS! (Here is the beautiful part) After it happened, as I was just making notes on the Standard Work Combination Sheet, the operator said to me, "Have you seen the zip-tie that they want me to put in the part? I think the drill press is just in the wrong place. Move it after inspection and I will never forget to drill it again." That was the easiest problem I ever had to solve!

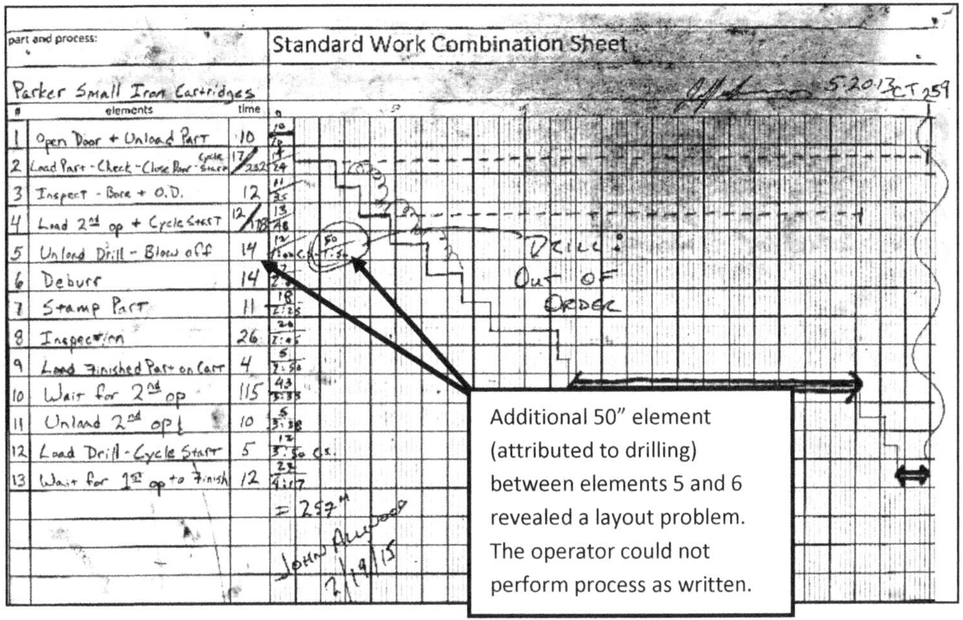

Figure 8-2: Missing Hole Standard Work

The new fix was to reorder the layout of the cell so that there could be no good reason for ever doing any task out of order.

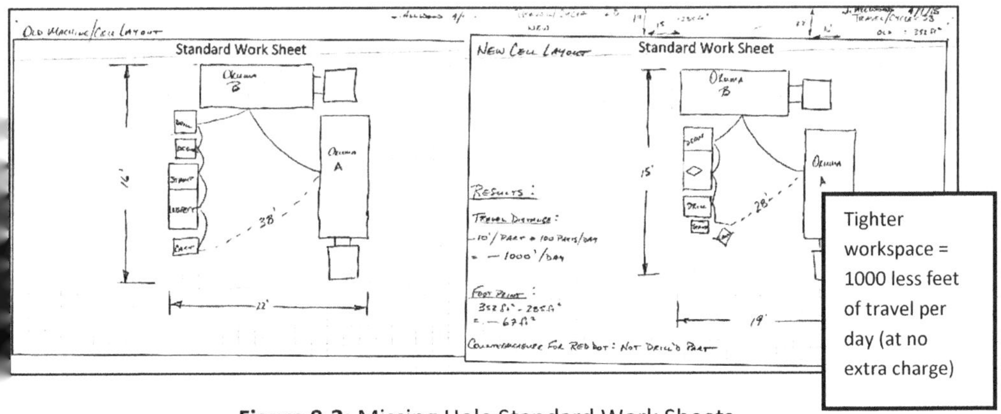

Figure 8-3: Missing Hole Standard Work Sheets

Pictured above (see figure 8-3) are the before and after Standard Work Sheets for the cell. The Drill has a new position downstream of the inspection step and the operator can verify his critical dimension without violating the appointed steps of the process. By the way, we also tightened the cell up, which had the effect of reducing operator travel by 1000' per day.

It is the notion of Autonomation that is at work here. It relates directly to the training examples (welding; de burring) in which it was the repetition of the exact steps in even a complicated process that creates the muscle memory required to perform successfully cycle after cycle. Change it up and expect varied results. I bristle whenever I hear operators say that everyone has his own way. I refuse to believe that if you do the same task many different ways, you will always get exactly the same results. That just doesn't make sense. I think the "each his own way" deal is just a result of our having not captured the "least waste way" on a document. However, document aside, if your layout supports the order in which the work must be done and as an operator steps through the physical space of the layout (cell), he is stepping past the tools or gauges needed at the time they are needed in order to create a muscle memory. The way I like to put it is to create such a layout so that if the operator passes a physical element/tool/machine, whatever, it will feel foreign for him NOT to unload/load; check; use the tool; etc.: compelled by the space and locations of the tools. Autonomation – Powerful stuff.

Proforma That's Really Not Proforma

There can be no excuse for not using Standard Work as a tool to help define and improve processes, not even if it doesn't exist yet. I have used "Proforma Standard Work" many times to help design processes before we put them together. In this example, we were machining large tubular exhaust manifold components on an HMC and then stepping them down a line of post processing operations that took over a week to complete (like a big dysfunctional inchworm of waste). We wanted to create a single piece flow cell that would include all those post processing steps in an "autonomational" flow of elements, but what might that look like (we all pondered)? In this case, we weren't going to be making anything new up. All the steps that were currently being performed on the parts would still need to be done; just in a continuous sequence. I set out to do a Time Observation and write the Standard Work for each of those steps as they were currently being performed. Then I did one of the things I enjoy doing the most with Standard Work. I made paper dolls (see figure 8-4).

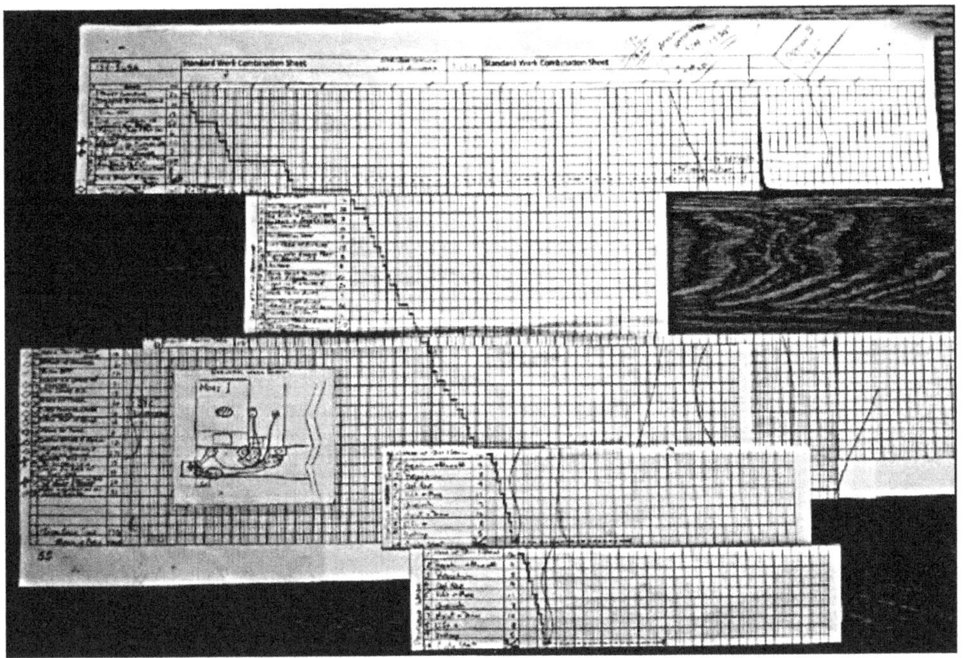

Figure 8-4: Proforma Standard Work

The sum of the elements came to 1400 seconds so, in March that was our cycle time prediction, which was kosher, because we already calculated our Takt Time to be 2400" for one shift. ("Looks like we will have time to make setups"). By May, we had our cell together and we were ready to fire up the first few single piece cycles. The actual observed cycle time came in at 1325," the delta being attributed to a "simulated single piece wash cycle."

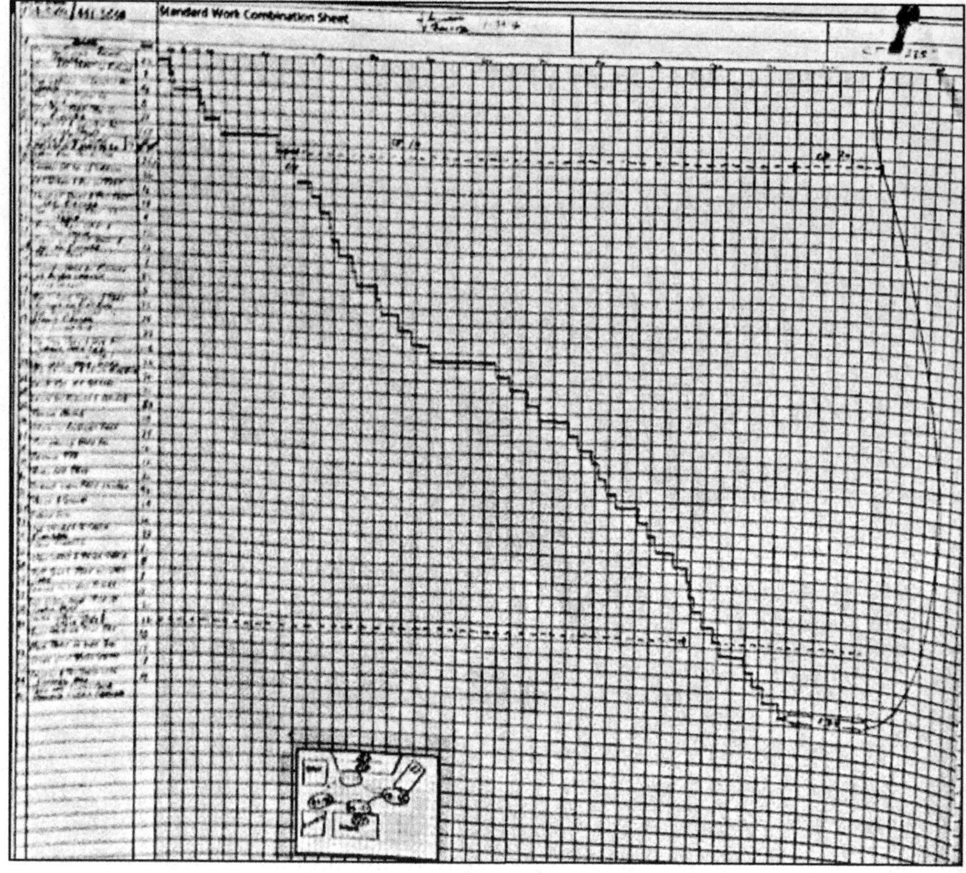

Figure 8-5: Actual Standard Work

The Standard Work has been rewritten and presides as the "plan" aspect of the Continuous Improvement cycle at the manufacturing cell (see figure 8-5).

The War Room Wall: Standard Work Cycle for a PPAP Process

Sometimes the need for a playbook pops up in the most interesting places. One corporation I worked for had a customer who dominated their sales volume, especially at one particular plant. As it turned out, for one reason or another, this customer decided to move the critical portion of their business to someone else, effectively closing the plant. Here was the good part. We could keep a slew of low volume part numbers (over 150, mostly for this company's service side) if we could execute their transfer from the plant that was closing to our company's remaining one. This was no small feat as "transfer" referred to a very top-heavy

PPAP process (Pre-Production Approval Process) compelled by this customer. I don't believe we were expected to survive it (but don't quote me).

The circumstances surrounding each part number were as varied as could be: some we had year's supply of. Some came in as "engineering changes". Some would be needed on assembly lines by the customer within the next month. All of it was one big moving target. There was much discussion about trying to take all 150-part numbers and try to describe a "firing order" and a plan of detail to support it. The ongoing misgivings expressed by those who were going to be charged with executing on the plan was that they would never really know what to work on and that the current requirements were only as reliable as the last "hot sheet" parts. Again with the "firing order"; but now there was created the largest spreadsheet I have ever seen. It was intended to be the tool with which to manage over 150 part numbers through an unwieldy 10-step PPAP process. I never thought that the order would hold up and I was afraid that this spreadsheet would become someone's maintenance nightmare. I was right about that. It was the feature of endless meetings. Better them than me.

My idea was to turn to the playbook. I knew that when not pressed, our company could work through PPAPs without much trouble, so I suggested that we just go slow and follow the tools. We were able to pin down the rate at which the customer was looking to see parts fully transferred from the closed facility to the remaining one (the Takt Time). It turned out to be three per week. The folks were worried because we had never performed to that rate before let alone over the course of the next 6 months. I asked what it took to do the steps of a PPAP and we worked out a Proforma Standard Work for both the engineering side and the quality side. Once we could see the Standard Work, we realized that each "flow" of tasks didn't have to be completed before another one was started. Only each segment of the process had to be completed before that operator could start another part number. We are talking about such tasks as bubble printing; writing a CNC program; creating the control plan; running three parts; a detailed layout inspection; filling out PPAP paperwork and filing. The team was initially correct: we had nowhere near the time per week to do all these tasks in series and then start again, but EACH OPERATOR could do their portion three times in a week easily. Once I realized this, I could see it was possible to "PULL" from a list of immediately required parts to transfer and always be working on what was relevant and never be working on something that the customer is not going to need anytime soon. They all looked at me as if I was a witch doctor or something and the V.P. of Operations told me to represent what I thought we could do so he could understand. I created the "War Room Wall" (see figure 8-6).

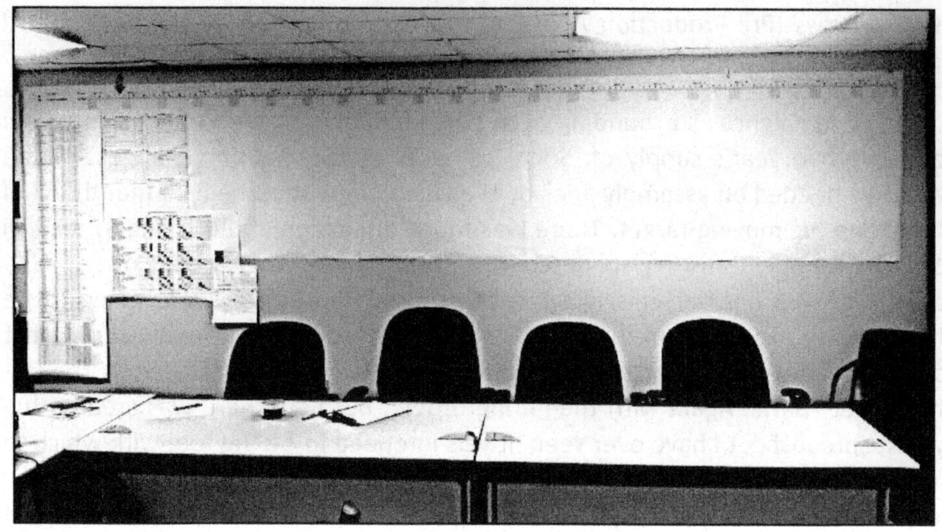

Figure 8-6: War Room Wall

It consisted (at this point) of a timeline for the transfer project over 6 months (the line at the top) and you can see the proforma Standard Work (in both SWCS and process map form) posted towards the left side of the picture.

Next, I wanted to create a visual under the timeline of us cycling three PPAPs per week, so I used red yarn to set up a tracking of performance over a scale of 1 to 4 (remember, we were shooting for three). The next picture was taken after we had been at it for 6 weeks. For each week, there is an Open Items to Complete Sheet tracking Red Dots of that week. You can see we started a little slow but by the end of week 6 we were sustaining the desired rate of three PPAPs per week (see figure 8-7).

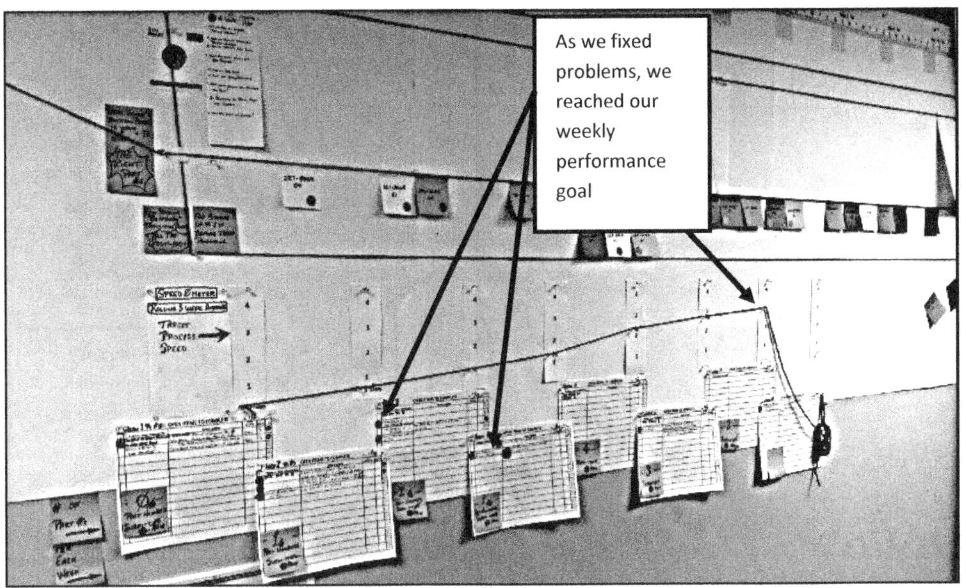
As we fixed problems, we reached our weekly performance goal

Figure 8-7: PPAP Cycles

An interesting thing happened by week 9 (see figure 8-8). You can see the red yarn line drops off to about 2.3 PPAPs per week. It seems that while the customer was saying that we would have to perform to three PPAPs per week, THEY could only process at their end (remember, it is THEIR unwieldy PPAP process in the first place) on the average 2.3 PPAPs. Our performance of 2.3 per week was our pulling at the perfect pitch of the customers Takt! There was a group of folks who were compelled to keep track of the spreadsheet, but at the end of the day, it was the Standard Work and Continuous Improvement processes that worked.

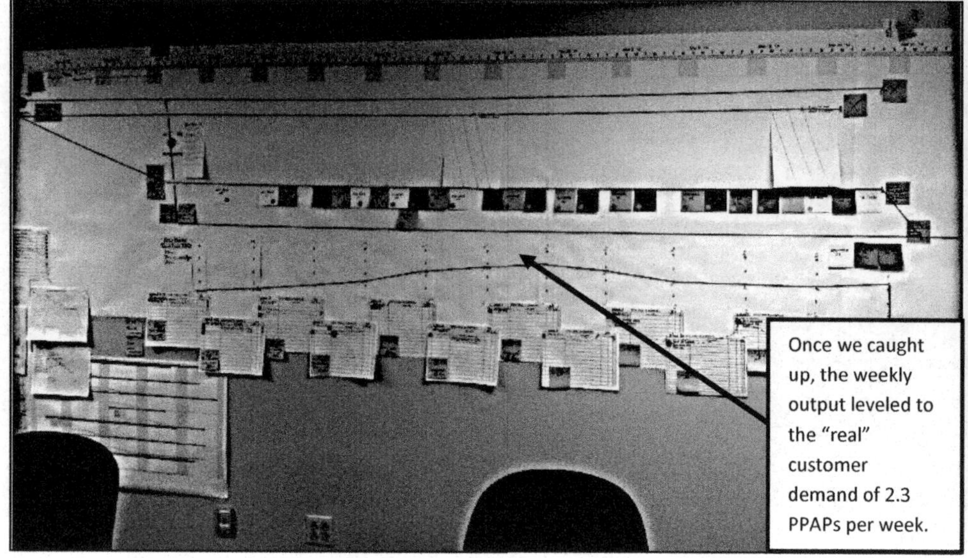

Once we caught up, the weekly output leveled to the "real" customer demand of 2.3 PPAPs per week.

Figure 8-8: The Finished Project

Our company performed all the PPAPs and we survived through a very tough economic time. My favorite part about how this all turned out (besides saving all the jobs) was that when the smoke cleared, I could just see the playbook template overlay on the War Room wall.

I don't know that I have ever lived an example of using the playbook tools in as much of a live or die business scenario as this one. I really did not know how scary the situation was until after the fact. I believe that is because I remained focused on the tasks of applying the tools and then looking to see what they were trying to tell me. It is a much more fruitful endeavor than fretting about the impossibility of the unknown.

The Playbook: Don't get caught out on the frontier without it

Fretting about the impossible unknown is a common activity, I'm afraid. At least, I have run into a fair share of it in my travels. It usually sounds like all the anticipated problems with or distant recollections of endeavors past that say, "We could never do that." It is a passive activity (I think that might be an oxymoron), and yet, it consumes a great deal of energy. It is a thought process that lingers in the NOUN end of the spectrum of life.

VERB-A-LIZE your thinking (I just made that word up!). Convert your ponderances into To Do's and live by a playbook. It is not like knowing where every journey will lead. It is like having a big pearly gate to step through that says,

"This is the way" at the beginning of every journey. My muscle memory for the tools just wills out and out pops the playbook template! I love that. It doesn't make me smart. It just makes me reliable.

Finally, Fear of change is often what drives inactivity. Choosing Standard Work; the verb, over noun-based activities like meetings, reporting, and pre-mortem predictions of doom can be an effective and therapeutic approach to handling fear of change in your organization. Replacing, "That will never . . ." and "We already tried that and . . ." with "What does that really look like" and "What would be possible if we didn't have to . . ." will lead to understanding and engagement. Every company that I have ever worked for, that came to such an epiphany, surprised itself with what they could do and actually moved their socio-cultural needle in the process. Feeding a fear of change with inactivity is a self-fulfilling prophesy of failure to fix root cause problems. Instead, go out and do. You'll feel better.

CHAPTER 9: Epilogue

Witness to History

Well, I guess I made it. My little project is almost in the bank (and thank you for everything, Bob!). I have very high hopes that I have accomplished a couple of things in so doing. I suppose that is, or should be, the goal of any writer, to accomplish something in the course of their writing; to provide the "takeaway" that will stick with the reader. Here is the first thing. I hope that I have conveyed that I consider myself a witness or a reporter of this material. The concepts within are represented as the very tools and application approaches that the O. G. Sensei(s) used to teach Bob, who taught us. Bob never claimed to have reinvented, refined, reprocessed, recalibrated, or applied any other kind of "re" to the tools and systems he learned two steps removed from the master's own hand. Nor have I.

It is this point that leads me to believe and present this material and the comments and anecdotes from Bob herein as having historical relevance towards LEAN and what it originally looked like when it came across the Pacific Ocean to America. Whatever else has been done in the name of creating LEAN tools and systems over the years, if it doesn't include Standard Work, it has strayed from the LEAN that Mr. Ohno created for Toyota. When I walk into places that claim to be practicing LEAN, I will forever ask about the Standard Work, and what happens next will tell me what I need to know. That litmus test I can trust and it works faithfully: forever and ever, amen.

WANTing to Change

Ownership / Executive Management in the organization still must WANT to change to a LEAN operating system. Without the drive of a basic WANT, the change will simply not succeed. A LEAN operating system cannot be translated into executive terms, on the executive's terms (see what I did there?). Executives; officers of the company; must embrace the NEW language of LEAN. You must embrace the new value sets that LEAN brings and learn to quantify those values on the company dashboard. Then you must communicate your own internalization through the layers of the organization by using the new visual controls to run the business. That is what WANTing to change looks like. However, constructing a false duality of LEAN by driving The New Initiative AND working to existing conventional reports / metrics / measures, will not convey internalization to the support staff and workforce. If the company's metrics and measurements don't complement the LEAN ways of doing things that have been put in place out on the shop floor, then those metrics will become their own drivers and LEAN will become a window dressing exercise. That does NOT look like WANTing to change.

Also, LEAN will take some time. People must go out and engage in the VERB of LEAN. There will probably have to be a shift in the types of activities that all of us do, but then again, if life for the support person is comprised of all his old duties under the old operating system AND new LEAN duties piled on top, then I would submit that the organization is in NOT WANTing mode. The least of your shop floor employees will be able to tell the difference instantly. No pulling the wool over those folk's eyes. They are the receivers of the WANTS of the company, performing the tasks supported and driven by the WANTS of the executive staff. I typically hold shop floor employees harmless in the failings of a company to gain traction in a LEAN initiative.

To the Lowly LEAN Trench Fighters out there

It is not just up to the folks in charge to WANT to practice LEAN. I know better than anybody that you will be shouldering the load. YOU, my LEAN trench fighting buddies, must WANT to do this stuff just like I have warned that your bosses have to AND sometimes its own reward will be the best you will get back (and occasionally a slap goes with it). Take heart; there is hope. If you really feel you are doing the right thing for the right reasons (and I believe I have) then all is well. The message of the following few paragraphs should see you through.

If there is anything significant that I have to contribute to budding LEAN trench fighters from my LEAN journey, it has come through trying, failing, and then trying to understand why. I am speaking to the organizational level of traction towards real change. I am speaking of my ability to compel ownership / management to WANT something different than they are used to running the company by (like Efficiency metrics and HOT Sheet shipping schedules). The fact is that I have never failed in the use and application of LEAN tools. NEVER. I have never written Standard Work and not gained many significant points of understanding about the process. I have never calculated a Percent Load, then performed to the Standard Work, and not satisfied the customer. I have never focused on Red Dots instead of a metric and not improved the actual productivity of an area. The tools have never failed me and by extension, I have never failed to accomplish what I wanted by using them. BUT, I HAVE failed to compel folks in charge to WANT to move in that direction. Sometimes agendas are more powerful. Sometimes an organization just isn't ready. The experience, however, is never without a very powerful, very valuable lesson.

Thus, any personal claim to success that I could really make comes from my ability to keep an ember of LEAN faith and belief alive within myself, even in LEAN adverse environments and especially in the face of failure, where everyone WANTS something different. That describes the majority of environments that I have worked in since leaving Bob and Tuthill.

Over time, I have nurtured my "ember of LEAN faith" and taken it with me everywhere I have worked. I have become pretty adept at appraising environments for their current value drivers and their level of change aversion, and as such, I don't always bring my ember to bear. The wrong socio-cultural combination can spell "fogedabodit" for LEAN's chances in the moment. But still, you must keep the faith. It is OK to lay low from time to time and do your "other" job. I don't know about the rest of you dog faces out there but this dogface has to eat and live indoors (most of the time), and that means staying employed. So, here is just one nugget of advice to all my LEAN trench-fighting friends out there: get another job! Don't get excited. Let me explain. I love practicing, coaching and teaching LEAN, but there is no experience like BEing and DEPENDING on LEAN. That is where real belief is created. That is where traction begins. You LEAN trench fighters can bring more impact to the world by creating and then OPERATING your own examples of LEAN systems than by just coaching other people to do so. You Change Agents out there must eventually get involved in managing a process. Look to put yourselves "out of work" so to say, and graduate to the operation at hand. I am always leery of the recommendation that a company create a full time office with staff to support a LEAN initiative. It will ultimately PREVENT internalization by the company at large as it creates the wrong dynamic. I have committed this sin personally while working at Tuthill. I loved being their Change Agent and I wanted that job to last forever. I think I did support the transition effectively as the champion of LEAN, but there came a point, in about year #7 or 8 where I found myself willing to DO the work FOR people: "I'll go sketch that Standard Work Sheet for you; I'll write the Standard Work for you; I'll do a Time Observation for you." I meant well. It was just because people were busy and didn't have time, but really, their wants were shifting. It was time for them to transition fully from DOing LEAN to BEing LEAN. And it was time for me to move on.

The Perfect Storm

As I have moved from company to company over the years of my work history, I have taken my ember with me into some pretty change-adverse environments. Sometimes I was the only one keeping warm by my ember. But, I have learned one more thing. Always look for the "perfect storm." I have seen this phenomenon more than once (and in more than one company). I am referring to a series of events and or people that have suddenly lined up to allow comprehensive change in that organization to occur. It may be the right burning platform. It may be the right communication of the burning platform. The departure or arrival of the right person or a changing of seats on the bus could bring it on. Whatever the case, the astute LEAN trench fighter is always on the lookout for a perfect storm, ready to exploit the opportunity and bring the tools in this book to bear. Paradigms will be broken and agendas melt as the tools start to compel anyone who sees what they can do and that will lead to creating LEAN systems. That is sometimes how journeys get started.

Cocktail Napkins and Binary Thinking

I hope that another thing that has translated in this book is that the tools don't require a computer. I do not hate computers, but I LOVE documents created by hand. There is a tacit personal connection, internalization, and credibility that are created when these documents are drawn by one's own hand. Don't take shortcuts. Preparing LEAN documents is as much about developing the muscle memory and internalization as it is producing working LEAN documents to show the way.

Also, be aware that LEAN documents work at two different levels of resolution. It is good to show the detail (and the math) that goes into a document (a Percent Load chart, a SWCS or SWS sheet), but, sometimes, it can be most effective to pan back to an elevation of say 30,000 feet and try to view the proportions of the document and understand what they are trying to tell you on a visual basis. Sometimes very informal and spontaneous document sketches (and I don't consider creating these to be taking shortcuts) have the greatest impact on a conversation.

I have had some of my most "epiphanizing" episodes featuring sketching LEAN documents by hand. I draw the reference from any number of invitational Kaizen Events I have traveled to and taken part in where groups of people would meet after hours to discuss the day's events. Bob was there many times. As we would all discuss, Bob would grab available writing surfaces (like cocktail napkins) and his favorite gel pen and start creating documents: Percent loads; Standard Work; Standard Work Sheet layouts. Without a computer or proper forms, resolution could be a bit rough, but still the relevant proportions were correct. I came to understand that "if – then" relationships could be gathered from documents as crude as cocktail napkin Standard Work and Percent Loads that could help us navigate the treacherous decision making waters of "what do we do next?" For example: A Takt Time is calculated. A process was observed and the cycle time was twice the Takt Time. You draw a Percent Load with a Takt Time line and a cycle time bar, which extends way up past the Takt Time line. Do we need to worry about by how much? No. We clearly don't have a process that can satisfy the customer, yet. We need to create a process with resources that will result in a cycle time equal to the Takt Time way. Do not pass go, do not collect $200. Work on a process. Save the finite calculations for when the cycle bar exceeds the Takt Time line by a smaller amount that you can take out of waste. Work on the layout. If the truly functional inputs of a decision can be boiled down to a yes/no level of resolution, then measuring how much is a waste of time. Go for the detection of the "yes or no" element, let that help you make your decisions, and move on! I call this binary thinking.

Binary thinking is like single piece flow for the brain. When you have clear, well defined requirements and each one is dependent on the one before, then when you come up light or missing elements, you have to go back and finish. You can't write Standard Work if you can't observe a stable process cycle. You can't create Percent Load if you don't know what your customer wants. You can't realize a red dot opportunity if you can't set forth a performance expectation to perform to and then SEE when you fail to hit it. In each of these cases, it doesn't matter how much you miss by, a miss is as good as a mile and you need not proceed to the next step without resolving the disconnect. Don't waste time calculating the miss. Binary Thinking. Look at it this way: Why use a calculated ratio in a report when a flashing red light would suffice? The most effective visual controls are structured this way.

Swan Song

So, I have maybe two handfuls of years left in the workforce. Bob has something less than that. Eventually, the LEAN message will have to survive without the two of us. At least we were able to leave this book behind. In the end, manufacturing will do what it does: muddle through one way or the other. As for Bob and I, we still see each other from time to time, usually for dinner. I hope THAT never ends. Over time, the focus of our conversations has shifted a bit, though. It is not that LEAN has become less important to each of us, but other things have become more important. We still talk about our jobs and LEAN, but we also talk about our families. We talk about people. We talk about God, as God has been good to both of us. Mostly anymore, I just like spending time with my dear friend.

ABOUT THE AUTHOR

John Allwood was introduced to the Toyota production system while working at Tuthill Pump, Alsip Illinois in the 1990's. That is where he met Bob Pentland, who is featured in Chapter 8 of Womack's "*LEAN Thinking*" book. In 1998 Bob was brought in as the company's LEAN consultant, and shortly thereafter, Tuthill Corporation began a ten year transformation to The Tuthill Business System; this under the watchful eye of Mr. Pentland.

John was appointed Tuthill Pump's Change Agent early in the journey, and served as such for the next eight years. He then transitioned into serving as Product Line Manager over and entire value stream including five machining cells and an assembly cell. After that, John took his LEAN show on the road, serving in engineering and management positions and found that LEAN was not very well understood from the Standard Work perspective, apart from the company where he had spent the previous decade. John also encountered and received training in several "LEAN interpretations", all of which conspicuously lacked in the focus on Standard Work. John has had to come up with creative ways in which to practice LEAN and promote Standard Work upstream as the opportunity has presented itself.

Over the years, John has also developed a strong sense of what it takes for an organization to make the transition to an enterprise that is BEing LEAN instead of just DOing LEAN things. The failure modes that have gotten in the way of change have provided as many valuable lessons as the successful endeavors have. The one thing that John has learned over the years is that DO-ing leads to BE-ing and that activity is the best medicine for dealing with the fear of change. This has led him to write the book, "Standard Work is a Verb: A Playbook for LEAN Manufacturing".

To learn more, visit www.standardworkisaverb.com

Glossary

Forward:

TPS – Toyota Production System – LEAN Operating System attributed to Taiichi Ohno

CT=TT – Cycle Time Equal to Takt Time: the goal of creating a process that has just enough resource to output to satisfy the customer's needs

SW – Standard Work – the documented least waste way of performing a work flow

Chapter 1:

LEAN – The term that was coined (not by the Japanese) that refers to the Toyota Production System

CAT CPS – Caterpillar Production System – Caterpillar's internalized LEAN Operating System

Chapter 2:

Takt Time – Time Available divided by Sold Units: the "beat" of the customer

Cell – a collection of equipment right sized and right equipped in a space to run a Standard Work production process

LEAN Journey – Referring to a transition from a former operating system to a LEAN operating system

Standard Work – The documented Least Waste Way to operate a process

Value Added / Non Value Added – actions or tasks that change the shape of raw material into something that the customer is willing to pay for, is referred to as "Adding Value". ANY tasks that aren't literally doing this – ANY – is referred to as "Non Value Added" in nature, and as such, is not something that a customer would pay for.

Hand Offs – disconnected flow / silo operations. Can typically be identified by piles of parts waiting in que to be operated on

Chapter 3:

Time Observation – objective time based documentation of a work activity

Six Sigma – a continuous improvement discipline- best known for problem analysis tools

SWCS – Standard Work Combination Sheet: Document that Standard Work is written on showing work element arrayed according to order and time

SWS – Standard Work Sheet: Document that Standard Work is written on showing layout of bird's eye view of a LEAN workflow

ISO – International Organization of Standardization. Home of the ISO 2000s certifications for manufacturing excellence

TS16949 – Technical Specification certification of excellence for automotive industry similar to the ISO certifications

WIP – work in process: partially finished material waiting in que for the next operation – unmanaged in process inventory (No Max Amount)

SWIP – the exact amount of inventory required to achieve single piece flow – managed in process inventory (very specific number of pieces required)

PPE – personal protective equipment

TO – Time Observation

Chapter 4:

Stop to Fix – a bias for fixing problems where and when they occur, even if process interruption is necessary

Chapter 5:

Time Available – Actual time allotted for making parts

Percent Load – a bar graph showing the comparison of cycle time to Takt Time OR average daily run time to Time Available (note: the two relationships are equal)

Chapter 6:

PDCA – Plan Do Check Act – A continuous improvement model often attributed to Demming

Expectations – The realistic number of parts a process can make based on written Standard Work during standard operating conditions (no unplanned process downtime)

Hour by Hour Sheet – Sheet used to express process expectations and then used to record actual output of process. Sheet used to indicate red dots (opportunities to fix something that is not working to expectations)

OITC – Open Items to Complete Sheet – used to record red dot opportunities and then record actions decided upon after asking why the red dot occurred

Red Dot – The indication that the actual output of a process differed from the expectation due to an unexpected departure from standard working conditions (tool/process problem that caused a stop to fix situation). These are to be considered opportunities because they present the opportunity to get better at executing the process. Without such opportunities, we cannot get better

Delta – the mathematical or spacial difference between an expectation of output and the actual output of a process

Andon – a signal of overall operating condition of a process, usually expressed by some color such as green for "standard operating condition" to red for "a non-standard condition is currently interrupting production" to yellow to signal "imminent process interruption"

Future State Behaviors – Physical behaviors driven by actual tasks and duties that support a changing operating system. These task driven behaviors are often new to folks and require commitment.

Chapter 7:

O.G. Senseis of Shingijutsu – These men are those folks mentioned in Womack's "LEAN Thinking" in chapter 8, *A Harder Case.* They were the fellas who took Ohno's teaching and synthesized it into the offering that hit Western awareness in the 1980's

ROM quote – Rough Order of Magnitude new business quote

AME – Advanced Manufacturing Engineer – Manufacturing Engineer typically responsible for new business quoting

KAIZEN – 5 day rapid improvement event – typically cross functional team chartered by an improvement plan and armed with LEAN tools

Cycle – The tasks and time required to complete a process of single piece flow. Is not limited to machine cycle time. Includes all post processing work elements.

Chapter 8:

Fundamental Tools: The Playbook – My own term for the approach to all LEAN situations in which the outcome is led by the application of the tools

Autonomation – word found in the original Singijutsu applications manual which refers to the notion of the management of the intentional order and layout of human elements through Standard Work aimed at eliminating variation. Properly applied, is as effective as "mechanical automation"

Proforma Standard Work – Standard Work written before the process has been tried and proven. Is often written by creating a string of known Standard Work elements performed elsewhere and as such, represent a process that has a high likelihood of matching the expectation of output.

HMC – Horizontal Machining Center – a common machine tool for metal cutting found in a work cell

PPAP – Pre Production Approval Process – a process of validating the production plan for making a part. Stems from the automotive world

Made in the USA
Coppell, TX
01 December 2020

42622993R00083